GEORGE ELIOT

SILAS MARNER
The Weaver of Raveloe

"A child, more than all other gifts
That earth can offer to declining man,
Brings hope with it, and forward-looking thoughts."
WORDSWORTH

Retold by: Katherine O'Doherty Jensen
Illustrations: Peter Bay Alexandersen
Series editor: Paulette Møller

EASY CLASSICS

Editorial assistance: Ulla Malmmose, Aschehoug

Cover layout: Jannie Andersen
Cover illustration: Lilian Brøgger

ISBN Denmark: 87-11-09010-3

Printed in Denmark by
Sangill Bogtryk & offset, Holme Olstrup

GEORGE ELIOT
(MARY ANN EVANS)

George Eliot was the name used by Mary Ann (Marian) Evans. She was born in 1819 in Warwickshire, England, the daughter of a carpenter. In 1828 she was sent to boarding school. Her mother died in 1836 and Marian then stayed at home to look after her father. She continued to educate herself in her spare time, language and philosophy being of particular interest to her. She also became an accomplished musician. In 1841 she moved from the countryside to Coventry where she met local intellectuals and began to work on translations. In 1851 she became managing editor of the *Westminster Review*. She moved to London, where she met G.H. Lewes. He was separated from his wife and unable to get a divorce. In 1854, he and Marian decided to live together, a socially difficult decision at that time. It was Lewes who encouraged her to turn from philosophy to fiction. During the twenty-four years they lived together, she wrote many major novels and other works, making her one of the greatest of English novelists. Among the best-known of her novels are: *The Mill on the Floss*, *Silas Marner* and *Middlemarch*. Lewes died in 1878 and George Eliot in 1880.

PART ONE

1

Silas Marner was usually bent down under a large heavy bag as he walked along. He carried his work with him on his shoulder when he made his way through the fields and the lanes around the village of Raveloe. He looked so pale, small and strange, that the dogs sometimes barked at him when he went by.

He never stopped to speak to anyone as he went along. Perhaps he did not see them. His large brown staring eyes did not see anything very clearly that was not close to them.

Nobody in the village of Raveloe knew exactly where he came from, except that it was a good distance to the north. Nobody even knew his family. There was not a person in those parts who could tell who his father and mother were. For during the fifteen years Silas Marner had lived in Raveloe, he had told no one about himself.

He was known as Master Marner, the *linen weaver*. You could give him *flaxen yarn* and pay him to weave it into one or more of his long rolls of strong linen cloth. But that did not mean that you felt that you could enter his door.

He lived by himself in a stone *cottage* near the village, not far from the edge of a *stone-pit*. The pit was no longer used. Most of it was full of water. The Raveloe

linen, cloth made from the flax plant
weaver, one who makes cloth
flaxen yarn, thread spun from *flax*, type of plant
cottage, very small house
stone-pit, large, deep hole from which stone is taken for building (in modern English: quarry)

boys sometimes came to play there and to look through the window of Silas Marner's cottage. They liked to listen to the *mysterious* sound of his *loom* and to see the strange small man bending over his work. If Marner noticed them, he would get down from his loom and, opening the door, would look at them in a way that made them run as fast as they could, back to the safety of the village.

Raveloe was an important-looking village, with a fine old church, a *rectory*, and some large stone houses with gardens, as well as many small cottages. It lay in a hollow, with wooded hills around it, quite an hour's journey on horseback from any of the main roads. It also had its own *inn*, the Rainbow. Not that Marner

mysterious, strange and difficult to explain (because the sound was not like any other machine known at that time - 1790's)
loom, machine for weaving cloth (see picture)
rectory, house that the minister of the church lives in
inn, place where food and drink are bought and enjoyed

had ever been into the village to take a drink at the Rainbow. He had never been inside the church. And it was clear to the young ladies of Raveloe that he would never ask any of them to marry him. Not, indeed, that any of them hoped he would.

The children called him 'Old Master Marner', though he was not yet forty years old. It was just that he was so *withered* and bent. There had been a lot of talk about him when he had first settled there as a young man.

One of the things that was said at the Rainbow was that Master Marner had a strange knowledge of *herbs*. Jem Rodney, the *mole-catcher*, had heard that Marner had given Sally Oates a bottle of brown water that he had made himself. When it turned out that the brown water had made Sally Oates much better than all the medicine she had got from the doctor, there was a lot more talk.

Who was this man who came from nobody knew where, with his secret *cures* and *charms*? But when people made their way out to the stone cottage with silver in their pockets to ask Master Marner for charms against their pains and aches, he refused.

No one believed him when he said that he had no charms. The hope that the weaver might be a Wise Man who would help his neighbours had slowly turned into fear. He might, people said, use his secret knowledge to do his neighbours harm. His trade was useful

withered, half dead, like a plant that is dried out
herbs, wild plants used as medicine, for their taste or nice smell
mole-catcher, person who catches moles, the skin of which was sold for making clothes (see picture, page 9)
cures, *charms*, things you eat, drink or useto make you well, or which you think will make you well

and his cloth was known to be very good. Otherwise, the children were told, it was best to keep well away from him.

These days, when his name was mentioned at the Rainbow, it was usually to remark that Master Marner must have a fine sight of money somewhere. For he was the only weaver for miles around, his work was well paid and everyone could see that he spent very little. 5

* * *

Marner had not always lived such a lonely life, of work and silence. Before he settled in Raveloe, he had woven his cloth for a *wholesale dealer* in a town far away from there. At that time, he had also had a close friend, William Dane, a young man slightly older than himself. He had even, for a time, been engaged to be married. The young woman was a servant called Sarah. Both of the young men were members of the *chapel in Lantern Yard*. And it was also through the chapel that Silas had met Sarah. 10 15

When he first began to grow very fond of Sarah, he had been afraid that his friendship with William might suffer. After all, he and William had gone everywhere together since they were young lads. But this fear was soon forgotten. Sarah did not mind the fact that William sometimes came with him on his Sunday visits to 20

wholesale dealer, person who buys goods in large numbers and sells them to shop-keepers
chapel in Lantern Yard, small group of religious persons, following the teachings of Calvin, calling themselves by the name of the place in which they meet and hold services

her home. The three of them soon found that they enjoyed each other's company.

It was his mother who had passed on to Silas her knowledge of herbs, several years earlier. Since she had 5 not much else to leave him, she had given him her little *store of wisdom* shortly before she died. And in the years after that he and William loved to walk through the fields outside the town searching for *foxglove, dandelion* and other herbs.

10 But Silas began to doubt whether it was right to use his knowledge of herbs. This was one of the points on which he liked to hear the views of his friend William. He had never found it easy to put his thoughts into words. William, on the other hand, loved to show that 15 he was wiser than everyone else.

Silas believed very strongly in the power of God. He began to think that herbs alone could not cure sickness. *Prayer* was needed too. Perhaps prayer was all that was needed, if one's belief in God was strong 20 enough. But his worries about this were pushed aside when an event occurred that changed his life in every way. For a time, Silas and William were kept very busy, day and night.

The senior *deacon* in the chapel had become serious- 25 ly ill. Being a *widower*, and having no children, the younger members of the chapel took it in turn to sit with him and look after him. Silas and William worked by day and took their turns with the deacon by night,

store of wisdom, knowledge, collected together
foxglove, dandelion, wild flowers, used as herbs (see picture)
prayer, talking to God, sometimes to ask for things
deacon, worker or officer in the chapel
widower, man whose wife is dead

the one taking over from the other at two o'clock in the morning.

One night, sitting by the bedside of the old man, Silas realised with fright that he could no longer hear the deacon's loud breathing. The candle was burning low. He lifted it to see the face clearly. The deacon was dead. He must have been dead for some time, in fact. His hands were very cold. Silas had fallen asleep! He looked at the clock. It was already four o'clock in the morning. Why had William not come?

Greatly worried, he immediately went to look for help. Soon several members of the chapel were gathered in the deacon's house. Silas had to return to his own home to start the day's work, sorry that he had no time to find William and discover the reason why he had not come.

By six o'clock that same morning, William stood in the door of Silas' home. The *minister*, Mr Paston, was standing just behind him.

"You are to come to a meeting at Lantern Yard."

"A meeting now? Why? Where were you? What is it about?"

"You will hear," was the only reply.

When Silas was seated at the meeting, Mr Paston took out a pocket-knife, showed it to Silas, and asked him if he knew where he had left that knife.

"I don't think I left it anywhere. As far as I know, I had it in my pocket the whole time," he replied.

The minister told him not to hide his sin, to confess it to the meeting and to *repent*. The knife had been found in the cupboard by the dead deacon's bedside - found in the place where the little bag of church money had been. Mr Paston had seen the bag the day before. William had been asked what he knew about this. He had explained that he had been ill during the night and unable to come to the deacon's house. Some hand had removed that bag since yesterday. Whose hand could that be, if not that of the owner of the knife?

Silas was *astonished* and quite unable to say anything. After a few moments, he was able to find some words.

"God will clear me. I know nothing about the knife or the money. Search me and search my home. You will find nothing but the three pound five that I have been saving to get married."

minister, senior officer in a chapel; clergyman in a church
repent, to be sorry for something you have done
astonished, shocked or surprised

The search was made. It was William who found the bag, tucked behind the chest of drawers in Silas' bedroom. He turned to Silas.

"It is best to hide your sin no longer."

"William," said Silas, "in the nine years that you have known me, have you ever known me to *tell a lie*?" 5

There was no reply. Suddenly, Silas went on to say, "I remember now - the knife wasn't in my pocket."

"I do not know what you mean," William replied.

The other people who were standing in the parlour crowded around the door and wanted to know what this was all about. Silas would say no more than, "I cannot bear it. I can say nothing. God will clear me." 10

Another meeting was held, following their return to Lantern Yard. According to the rules of the chapel, the members had to work out a matter of this kind for themselves. It was forbidden to bring the case to a court of law. It was decided that they should all pray together, after which they would *draw lots*. 15

Silas knelt with the others, ready to trust that God would look after him, even though his trust in his friend William had been broken forever during the last hour. To his utter amazement, the lots declared that Silas Marner was *guilty*! 20

The minister got up to make a speech. Silas listened, stunned to hear that he was no longer to be a member of the chapel. Only when he had confessed his sin and paid back the stolen money could he again be a member. 25

tell a lie, say something that is not true
draw lots, decide something by chance, using straws, sticks, dice or anything else for this purpose
guilty, to have done something that is wrong or evil

Silas rose to leave the meeting with the others. On his way out he spoke to William Dane in a low shaking voice.

"The last time I used my knife was when I cut a strap for you. I don't remember putting it in my pocket again. **You** stole the money and you planned to lay the sin on me. But you may do well for yourself anyway. For there is no God of justice to rule the earth according to what is right."

The few members who heard these last words were very shocked. Silas Marner not only stole money, he no longer believed that God was just and fair!

Marner left the meeting. Sarah will cast me off as well, he thought to himself as he made his way home.

If she believed him, she too would have to lose her trust in the chapel at Lantern Yard and in their friends. But to lose your trust in God and man seemed to him to be a form of madness. He had no hope left.

When he reached his home, he sat alone for the rest of the day, unable to move or think. When he awoke the next day, thoughts began to crowd into his head. He stopped himself from thinking by getting into his loom to work. After some hours, the minister and one of the deacons appeared at his door with a message from Sarah. She considered that her engagement to Silas was at an end. He heard the message in silence. When they left, he returned to his loom again.

In little more than a month from that time, Sarah was married to William Dane. Not long afterwards it was known to the chapel at Lantern Yard that Silas Marner had left the town.

* * *

There was nothing in Raveloe to remind Silas Marner of his past. It seemed to him that life there was like a life in a new land, compared to that of the busy town. And when there was nothing or nobody to remind him of his past, the past itself slowly became like a bad dream. The only fixed point now in Silas Marner's life was his work - his loom and his weaving.

He seemed to weave, like the spider, without thought. He sometimes worked far into the night to finish the linen for the Cass household, for Mrs Osgood or for other people at the big houses. He would finish it earlier than they expected. But he never asked himself why he did this.

In Raveloe, Silas was paid in gold. This had been quite new to him at first. The wholesale dealer in his native town had paid him far less money by the week. But every penny had had its purpose then. Much of it had gone to the *charity work* at the chapel.

Silas felt surprised the first time he had five bright *guineas* put into his hand. No one expected a share of them. He found that he liked the feel of them, however. He liked to look at their bright faces, which were all his own, on his way home. He especially liked to look at his money in his hand if it was growing dark as he found his way back to his cottage. It seemed to him that they looked brighter then.

Gradually the guineas, the crowns, and the half-crowns grew to a heap. The size and shape of the heap had come to mark off his weaving into periods of time. He wanted the heap to grow into a square. Then to a larger square. He began to spend less and less money on his own wants.

In the night, when his work was done, Silas took out his coins to enjoy their company. He handled them, counted them and arranged them into *regular* shapes.

charity work, helping poor people who have no money
guineas, gold coins (old)
regular, here: with sides that are the same length (see picture)

He had taken up some bricks from the floor underneath his loom. Here he set an iron pot that contained his guineas and silver coins.

The very smallest of the silver coins were picked out with care when he needed to buy some food or other small items. And the level of the gold in the iron pot rose higher with his years of work.

When the iron pot could no longer hold all the coins, he made two large leather bags which fitted well into the hole in the floor. The sight of the golden guineas, pouring out of the bags at night time, was the *gleam* of joy in his life. He treated them fondly as he counted them, almost as though they were unborn children.

His thoughts were with his loom and his money when he made his way through the fields and lanes. After fifteen years in Raveloe, he never wandered towards the hedges in search of the familiar herbs. That was a mistake he had made only once, the time he had felt such pity for Sally Oates. Marner had not known then that his offer of help would bring so many people

gleam, ray of light

to his door. But the sight of people crowding at his door had brought back a memory that he could not bear. He had sent them all away, leaving himself more *lonely* than ever.

5 About Christmas time of that fifteenth year, a second great change came over Silas Marner's life.

2

Squire Cass was the most important man in the village of Raveloe. He lived with his four sons in the Red House, a large house with stone steps in front and 10 stables behind, nearly opposite the church.

Other families in the village also lived in fine houses and had large farms. There were the Osgoods for instance, just a little higher up the street. But Squire Cass was the only *landowner* in Raveloe who also rent-15 ed out smaller farms to *tenant* farmers. And his tenants brought their complaints to him, quite as if he had been a lord. Everyone called him the Squire.

The rich families in Raveloe ate and drank very well indeed. Even in winter-time they seemed to lead a 20 carefree life. In the dark season, when there was little work to be done, and the hours were long, parties were held that sometimes lasted for days.

A party might start at the Cass's house. And when the guests felt that the portions of beef, the hams, pork-

lonely, on one's own with nobody to talk to
squire, gentleman who owns a lot of land
landowner, person who owns land, usually land that is used for farming or building
tenant, person who pays money for the right to use something that they do not own, such as land or a house

pies or *barrels of ale* were not quite as many or as fresh as they had been, they only had to walk up the street, where the feast continued at the Osgoods'.

It must be said that the food at the Osgoods' usually looked somewhat better than at the Red House. It was 5 always laid out so beautifully, that it looked *more excellent* at any rate. Here, as the guests well knew, was the woman's touch. And that was what was sadly missing in the Cass household.

For the Squire's wife had died long ago. His neigh- 10 bours knew very well that this was the reason why he was so often to be seen spending an evening at the Rainbow. Some said that the loss of their mother was also the reason why the Squire's sons were not turning out as well as might be expected - the older ones at any 15 rate. Perhaps it was too soon to say how the younger boys would turn out.

The second son in particular, Dunstan Cass, was not a popular young man. He seemed to do no work at all. Sometimes he *disappeared* from home for days, even 20 weeks, at a time. Soon after he came back there would be tales of his card-playing, sporting and drinking.

barrels of ale, wooden tubs of beer (see picture)
more excellent, very much better
disappeared, went away, without anybody knowing where

When he was at the Rainbow, he seemed to enjoy his drink all the more when other people went without any.

It would be a terrible pity, the neighbours thought, if Godfrey were to turn out like his younger brother. Master Godfrey, being the eldest son, would own the farm and the lands some day. He was a fine, open and pleasant young man. At one time everyone was saying what a lovely couple he and Miss Nancy Lammeter would make. A young lady brought up like Miss Nancy would make a wonderful change at the Red House. And what a saving a daughter-in-law like that would be to the Squire.

But things might not turn out that way at all. It was quite clear now that Godfrey was no longer the smiling young man that he had been just a couple of years ago. Something was wrong. He had been away from home for days and days together. And for the last year or more now, people had been wondering whether he still had a chance with Miss Nancy. It was difficult to say, but interesting all the same to keep an eye on.

It was just as well that the neighbours did not know what was going on in the parlour of the Red House on this particular day in November during that fifteenth year of Silas Marner's life in Raveloe.

"Just shake yourself *sober* and listen, will you?"

Godfrey was speaking angrily to his younger brother, Dunstan.

"I must hand over Fowler's *rent money* to father. He

sober, the state of not being drunk or not having taken too much alcoholic drink
rent money, money paid for the right to use something, such as land or a house

doesn't know that I collected it. I'll have to give it to him very soon. Or else I'll have to tell him that I gave it to you. So see about getting the money quickly, will you?"

"Oh!" said Dunstan, "Why don't you get the money yourself? Save me the trouble." 5

"Put down that drink for a minute, while I'm talking to you."

Dunstan did not put down his glass. He put his feet up on a chair. 10

"Take it easy. I can get you turned out of house and home any day." He smiled as he went on, "I might just tell father how you married Molly Farren without his knowledge. First, you could not wait to marry her. Then, you were so unhappy because you couldn't live with a *drunken* wife!" 15

Godfrey bit his lip and said nothing.

"I could slip into your place here any day," Dunstan continued in a lazy voice. "You'll get the hundred pounds for me - I know you will." 20

"How can I get the money? I haven't a *shilling*!"

"Borrow it from old Kimble."

"Uncle Kimble won't lend me any more. I can't ask him."

"Well, then, sell Wildfire," suggested Dunstan. "You only have to ride him over to the *hunt* at Batherley tomorrow. You'll easily get a hundred pounds for such a fine horse." 25

"And get back home at eight o'clock in the evening,

drunken, under the influence of alcohol
shilling, small coin
hunt, a sport in which a fox is chased by dogs (foxhounds), followed by persons riding on horses

splashed with mud from head to toe. I can't do that. I'm going to Mrs. Osgood's birthday dance."

At last, Dunstan put down his glass on the table. Turning slowly to face his brother, he said in a high sil-
5 ly voice:

"Ah! We are going to dance with Miss Nancy, are we? We are going to promise never *to be naughty* again, are we? And..."

"*Hold your tongue* about Miss Nancy, you fool," said
10 Godfrey, turning red in the face. "I might as well tell the Squire everything myself," he went on. "He'll know sometime, anyway. Molly has been saying that she is going to come and tell him everything herself."

"She has what?" Dunstan sat up straight in his chair.
15 "She has. And she means it. She'll turn up here some day. Don't think my *secret* is worth any price. When you keep asking for more money, I have nothing left to keep Molly happy. I might as well tell the Squire all about her myself."

20 This time, Dunstan began to fear that he had pushed Godfrey too far.

"Yes, well, whatever you want. I'll just have another drink, anyway," he said, as he got up to press the bell.

Godfrey stood with his back to the fire, trying to
25 think things out. If he were to tell the Squire himself, it was certain what would happen. He would be turned out of his home and would lose his *inheritance*. Not only

to be naughty, to do silly or bold things, as grown-ups see it
hold your tongue, do not talk
secret, something that is only known by one person or a few persons and which you do not want other people to know
inheritance, here: money, land and other things of value that are left to a person when someone dies

that, he would never see Nancy Lammeter again. There would be no future for him at all if he followed that path.

A servant appeared with some ale for Dunstan, interrupting Godfrey's line of thought for a moment. 5

But as long as he said nothing to the Squire, there was at least a hope that something might work out. He had his home, his food, the wine he loved, although some of the time he lived in terror of the day when the Squire would find out about Molly. 10

The idea of selling his horse began to seem like a better way out of his problems. He could not share these thoughts with Dunstan, of course. The only way to deal with him was to keep up the quarrel.

"It's just like you to talk about my selling Wildfire - 15 the best horse I have ever had in my life. You're not even sorry to see the stables emptied. You'd sell yourself, just to give someone a *bad bargain*."

"Yes, yes - I'm good at selling all right," replied Dunstan. "Why not let me sell Wildfire for you? I can ride 20 him over to the hunt tomorrow, if you like."

"Trust you with my horse!"

"As you please," said Dunstan, picking up Godfrey's *whip* and rapping it on the chair as though he hadn't a care in the world. 25

"It's you that has to pay Fowler's rent money," he went on. "And you are the one who told the Squire it was never paid. It has nothing to do with me. I was just trying to be helpful."

bad bargain, something bought which is not good value for the money paid
whip, a lash with a handle, used for making a horse run faster

This last remark made Godfrey feel like taking his whip from Dunstan's hand, and hitting him with it. But when he spoke, he tried to keep the anger out of his voice.

5 "Well, no tricks about the horse, eh? You'll sell him fair, and hand over the money?"

"I thought you'd see reason," said Dunstan, getting up to go. "I'll get you a hundred and twenty pounds for him."

10 "Take care that you *stay off the drink* tomorrow. Or else Wildfire might be the worse for it."

"Don't worry. I always fall on my feet."

And with that remark, Dunstan slammed the door behind him, leaving Godfrey to his own thoughts. How
15 he hated trusting that brother of his with the sale of his horse. But he could not give up the chance of seeing Nancy again tomorrow.

Perhaps she was still a little bit fond of him. But she did seem to know that he had tried to keep out of her
20 way several times during the last year or so. How could he have been so foolish as to get himself trapped into a secret marriage with Molly Farren, of all people?

Just because Dunstan and the other young men had told him what a wonderful woman Molly was, he had
25 thought himself lucky! He knew nothing about her drinking and her *opium* habit until he was married to her. And now just the thought of her made him shiver. That was another reason for keeping away from the hunt tomorrow. It was near Batherley, the market-town
30 where Molly lived.

* * *

stay off the drink, do not drink alcohol
opium, very strong narcotic drug

Dunstan Cass set off for Batherley the next morning, riding slowly along the lane that led to the Stone-pit. As he drew near, he could see the red muddy water high up in the pit. A moment later, he could hear the noise of Silas Marner's loom.

That fool of a weaver, he thought to himself. He has a great deal of money hidden somewhere. He had heard talk of that for years. Now why had he never thought of suggesting to Godfrey that he should borrow from old Master Marner?

The young Squire should be able to frighten the weaver into lending him more than enough. There would be plenty left over for his younger brother. And Godfrey would like to hear any plan that might save him from having to sell his favourite horse.

He was just about to turn Wildfire around. But why should he help Godfrey in this way? He liked the important feeling of having a horse to sell. He decided to keep the idea for future needs. And he set out for Batherley at a faster pace.

Bryce and Keating were sure to be at the hunt that day. And Bryce was a young man who had long had his eye on Wildfire. It would be easy enough to sell the horse.

Everything went according to plan. It was short work to arrange the sale. The *brandy* in his pocket *flask* was brought out to seal the bargain. One hundred and twenty pounds would be paid when Wildfire was delivered, safe and sound, at the Batherley *stables*.

brandy, strong alcoholic drink, sometimes called cognac
flask, bottle for carrying drinks out of doors
stables, buildings in which horses or other animals are kept

Dunstan thought it might be wise for him to give up the day's hunting and ride over to the Batherley stables right away. He could wait there for Bryce to return, and then hire a horse to take him home with the money in
5 his pocket. But then, why wait? Why not have a good run on a fine horse first? The way Wildfire took the fences, he and his rider would be admired by all.

That day, however, Dunstan took one fence too many. The horse was *pierced* by a *hedge-stake*. And
10 while Dunstan picked himself up unhurt, poor Wildfire turned painfully on his side and panted his last breath. Dunstan had fallen behind in the hunt just a few minutes before. Luckily there was no one around to see him now.

pierced, penetrated
hedge-stake, heavy long piece of wood with a sharp top, one of many placed in a line of bushes to make a fence (see picture)

As soon as he could see that Wildfire was dead, he dusted himself off and took a little more brandy. Then he made his way as fast as he could towards the woods on the right. He could make his way to Batherley from the far side of the woods, without meeting any of the other members of the hunt who would soon be coming up behind him.

He did not mind so much about taking the bad news home to Godfrey, now that he had the new plan about Marner's money to offer instead. And that plan seemed to him to be better and better the more he thought about it.

It was nearly four o'clock in the afternoon by the time he reached the far side of the wood. There was a *mist* coming down. But he could see that he was not very much farther from home than he was from Batherley. Why turn up at the Batherley stables with muddy boots, trying to explain himself and borrow a horse? He could not pay for the hire of a horse to take him home, now that he had no horse to sell. He might as well take the road home. So, buttoning up his coat, he grasped his hunting whip firmly and set off down the road.

A young gentleman like Dunstan was not at all used to going along a road on foot. He hoped he would not meet anyone he knew. He would be laughed at, and he would have to give an *explanation*. It helped when he thought of his new plan to borrow from old Marner. It also helped to *rap* the tops of his boots with his very

mist, thin fog, making it very hard to see
explanation, to tell or be told the reason why something happened
rap, knock

fine whip as he *strode* along. This gave him the feeling that he was in charge of the situation, and that nothing surprising had happened.

The whip belonged to Godfrey, and he had taken it without asking. It had Godfrey's name cut in deep letters on the gold handle. But when he held it in his hand, nobody saw that. Now that it was getting dark, he had to find his way by dragging the whip along the low bushes at the side of the road.

At last he found himself in the lanes of Raveloe. Luckily he had not met anyone. He went more carefully now, feeling his way with the whip, waiting for the break in the hedge near the opening of the Stone-pit. Rain had come down as well as the mist and the lane was very *slippery*.

It was a gleam of light, however, that told him that the Stone-pit was close by. It came from Silas Marner's cottage. Yes, of course it was old Marner's cottage! What could be better than to visit the old fellow now. See what he was like. He might even see how he reacted to the idea of lending money. At the very least, he could lend a *lantern*.

Dunstan knocked loudly on Marner's door. There was no reply. The cottage was silent. The old *miser* would never have gone to bed, leaving a light on. Dunstan shook the door. To his surprise, it opened, and he found himself in front of a bright fire.

The fire on the hearth lit up every corner of the cot-

strode, walked fairly fast with long steps
slippery, easy to slip and fall on
lantern, lamp covered with a case for using out of doors
miser, person who saves his money and hates to spend any

tage - the bed, the loom, the three chairs and the table - and showed him that Master Marner was not there. Nothing could have been more inviting to Dunstan at that moment than the sight of the bright fire. He walked in and sat himself by it at once. 5

There was a delicious smell, too, that made him realise how hungry he was. A small piece of pork was slowly roasting above the fire. Unfortunately, it was far from cooked yet. It hung from the kettle hook by a string that had been passed many times through a large door- 10 key. This must be to prevent it cooking too quickly while the owner was away. But where on earth could the old weaver be, at this hour of the evening, and in this weather?

Perhaps he had gone outside to collect *fuel*, and had 15 slipped into the Stone-pit. If he was dead, who had a right to his money? Who would know where his money was hidden? Dunstan's next thoughts followed quickly. Who would know that anybody had come and taken it? Where could the money be? He looked over 20 at the bed. That was a possibility. It could also be in a hole in the floor.

The bricks in the floor stood out clearly in the firelight, covered by a thin layer of sand. There was one spot, and one only, which was quite covered with sand 25 - sand that showed the marks of fingers. It was just under the loom.

Dunstan *darted* to the spot, swept away the sand with his whip, and put the thin end of the whip between the bricks. They were loose. He lifted up two bricks as 30

fuel, wood or coal, used for keeping a fire going
darted, moved very fast

quickly as he could. He had found what he was looking for.

What could there be but money in those two leather bags? And from their weight, they must be filled with guineas. Quickly he felt around the hole to be certain that it held no more. Then he put the bricks back and spread the sand over them again.

Hardly more than five minutes had passed since he had entered the cottage. But it seemed to him like a long time. Dunstan was very frightened as he got to his feet with the bags in his hand. He must leave as quickly as possible. Time enough to think about what to do with the bags when he was outside again.

He quickly closed the door behind him. No light must show him up, if anyone should be passing by. The rain and the darkness had got thicker. It was going to be difficult, walking with a bag in each hand and a whip as well. But as soon as the cottage was behind him, he would be able to take his time. So he stepped forward into the darkness.

3

When Dunstan Cass left the cottage, Silas Marner was not more than a hundred yards away. He was making his way along the lane that led from the village. He had a sack on his shoulders to keep off the rain and a lantern in his hand to help him find his way in the mist.

He was thinking of his supper. It would be hot and tasty. And it would cost him nothing. He would sit in front of his fire warming his feet, enjoying the taste of roast meat and looking forward to the moment when he would take out his bright guineas.

That very day Miss Priscilla Lammeter had given him a little piece of pork as a present when she paid for the fine roll of linen that he delivered to her. And Silas only ate roast meat for supper when, now and again, it had been given to him as a present.

But his walk that day out to the Lammeters' house had not brought him through the village. He should have gone there to collect some thin *twine* that he needed to set up a new piece of work in his loom early the next morning. He remembered the twine while he was setting out the things he needed for the next day's work, waiting for his supper to cook.

In ordinary weather it would only take him twenty minutes to get from the cottage to the village and back. Silas had decided to go at once to buy the twine. He hated to delay his work in the mornings. It might take

twine, string made strong by twisting threads together

longer in this weather, of course. He pulled his supper to the very edge of the fire. But his lovely bit of pork was tied to the door key. Leaving it there would mean that he could not lock his door. He decided not to let this worry him. Hardly anyone had come out to the cottage during the last fifteen years. And who would come out at this hour of the evening, and in this weather?

The weather was very bad, worse than he had thought. But now that he was nearly back at the cottage again, he felt pleased to have collected his twine and to have his supper waiting for him. The fire sent out a welcome glow of heat as he opened his door. He shut the weather out as fast as he could, put his sack in front of the *hearth* to dry, moved his pork nearer to the centre of the fire and sat down to warm himself.

As soon as he was warm again, he began to think it would be a long while to wait for the sight of his guineas until after supper. How nice it would be to enjoy the sight of glinting gold in the light of the candle and the flickering fire. He took his candle and placed it on the floor beside his loom. His short-sighted eyes noticed no change, as he swept away the sand. He removed the bricks.

The sight of the empty hole made his heart jump. It was a moment of pure terror. Silas could not believe that his gold was gone. He felt with his hand in every corner of the hole, not trusting his eyes. Then he held the candle down in the hole. There were still no leather bags. He was trembling so much, he had to put the candle down on the floor. He held his hands to his

hearth, floor of the fireplace

head, trying to hold it steady so that he might think.

He must have put the gold somewhere else. But where? He began to search in every corner. He turned his bed over and shook it, tried behind the chair, inside the old brick oven that he never used. When there was no other place to look, he tried the hole once more. Finally, he put his hands to his head again and gave a wild strange cry. He was beginning to believe the awful truth. He made his way over to the seat of his loom and sat down.

He had not hidden his gold anywhere else. There was no point at all in looking and hoping. The truth was that he had *been robbed*. A *thief* had been here.

This thought gave him a little strength. After all, a thief could be caught and made to give the gold back. The thief must be caught. That was it. He must do something as soon as possible. He would make his way

been robbed, had something stolen
thief, person who steals

to the Rainbow. That was the place where all the important people in Raveloe would be on a night like this. He would tell the clergyman, the policeman and Squire Cass. They would find the thief.

Silas ran from the cottage as fast as he could, forgetting the sack to cover his head. He did not bother locking his door, for he had nothing left to lose.

The rain was coming down more heavily now and it was not possible to run all the way. Who could the thief be? And when had he come? Not earlier in the day. His door had been locked then. It must be Jem Rodney, the *poacher*. A poacher was not an honest man. And when Silas met him in the lanes or the fields, he had often made a joke about the weaver's guineas. Jem Rodney would be caught, and the gold would be given back. Silas tried to make his legs go faster. At last, he could see the yard in front of the Rainbow and a flicker of light within.

But what Silas did not know was that none of the important people of Raveloe were in the Rainbow that night. The young people, like Godfrey Cass, were dancing at Mrs Osgood's birthday party. Their parents, including those whom Silas wanted to see, were drinking Mrs Osgood's spirits and water, further up the street.

All the other usual visitors at the Rainbow that night had crowded into the kitchen to warm themselves at the fire. Suddenly, all their talk and laughter stopped dead. And all eyes turned to take in the sight of Silas Marner in the Rainbow, standing there with his

poacher, person who traps and catches animals on land that belongs to another person - poaching is a form of stealing

pale face and staring eyes, dripping wet and not saying a word.

"Master Marner," said Mr Snell the innkeeper, at last breaking the silence, "what is your business here?"

5 "Robbed," gasped Silas, "I've been robbed. And I want Squire Cass, the police, the *Justice*, and Mr Crackenthorp, the clergyman."

"Get a hold of him, Jem," said the innkeeper to Jem Rodney, who was sitting nearby, "I think he must be *off*
10 *his head*."

"Get a hold of him yourself, Mr Snell," replied Jem, who was not sure whether the figure before him was that of Master Marner or that of a *ghost*. "He's been robbed. And by the look of him, maybe he has been
15 *murdered* too."

"Jem Rodney!" said Silas, turning to him, "It was you who stole my money. Give it back to me and I will not set the police after you."

"Me! Stole your money?" said Jem Rodney, very
20 angrily.

"Come now, Master Marner" said the innkeeper, taking hold of Silas by the shoulder. "Get your coat off now. Sit down by the fire and try to talk like a *sensible* man."

25 "Now then, Master Marner, speak out," continued Mr Snell, when room had been made for Marner in front of the fire.

It felt very strange to Silas to sit in front of a fire that

justice, here: person with the job of punishing those who break the law
off his head, mad (not sane)
ghost, someone who comes back after they have died
murdered, killed by a person
sensible man, man with good sense who does not do silly things

was not his own and to talk to a lot of people who listened more and more carefully to what he had to say. A lot of questions were asked. He answered as well as he could, telling all that he knew about what had happened. 5

"Well," said the innkeeper, when he had finished, "I can tell you this, Master Marner. It was not Jem Rodney who stole your money while you were out and your door was unlocked. For he has been sitting here the last few hours drinking his ale." 10

"Yes, that is quite right," added Mr Macey, the *tailor* and *clerk of the parish* church. "Let us not have any *accusing* of *innocent* people, Master Marner."

These words reminded Silas of the time when he himself had been accused of a crime that he had not 15 committed. Getting up, he went over to Jem Rodney and, after looking at him closely, he said, "I was wrong. Yes, yes - I ought to have thought... I do not accuse you, Jem. I won't accuse anybody. I was just trying to think of where my guineas could be." 20

"How much money was there in the bags, Master Marner?" Mr Macey asked, in a way that suggested that he was beginning to feel sorry for Marner.

"Two hundred and seventy-two pounds, twelve shillings and six-pence, last night when I counted it," said 25 Silas, sitting down again.

tailor, person who makes suits of clothes
clerk of the parish, person who does paper work and other work for the local church
accusing, (to accuse:) to blame someone for doing something that is wrong, evil or against the law
innocent, not guilty, not having done something that is wrong, evil or against the law

That was a great deal of money. But, it was agreed after some discussion, it would not be too heavy a load to carry. A *tramp* must have been into the cottage while Marner was out buying his twine. He would not have noticed anything on his return. For, as Mr Macey pointed out, Master Marner had eyes like an insect that had to look so closely at things, he didn't see much at a time. It was agreed that two of the men present should go with him to find the policeman. Afterwards, they would go out to the cottage and look in every corner.

And so poor Silas turned out into the rain again, Mr Macey and a Mr Dowlas walking beside him. Walking up the village street in the company of other people was something that Silas had never once tried during all the years he had lived in Raveloe.

* * *

When Godfrey Cass returned home from Mrs Osgood's party late that night, his mind was full of thoughts of Nancy Lammeter. She looked so lovely when she danced. Godfrey felt such a fool for having lost the chance of asking her to marry him.

He was not very surprised to hear that Dunstan was not home yet. It was just like him to have decided to stay the night in Batherly. He would not want to ride home in that weather. Perhaps he had not even sold the horse yet.

The next morning the whole village was excited about the story of the robbery. Godfrey, like everyone

tramp, person who goes from place to place, having no home, asking for food or selling things

else that morning, was busy hearing the latest news, talking about the robbery and visiting the cottage out at the Stone-pit.

The rain had washed away all foot marks. But one man had found a *tinder-box* not far from the cottage, half sunk in the mud. This was just the kind of tinder-box a tramp or a *pedlar* would carry around to light his pipe or to light a fire. Mr Snell had then remembered that it was not long since a pedlar had passed through the village.

Soon everyone was trying to remember exactly what the pedlar had looked like, who he had talked to, when he had been there, what he was selling and what clothes he had worn.

"Did he wear earrings?" Mr Crackenthorp had wanted to know. He was seated in the best parlour at the Rainbow, discussing the matter with Squire Cass and Mr Snell. It was not long before everyone in and near the Rainbow was trying to remember and then to describe the pedlar's earrings.

Anyone who had bought anything from the pedlar took it with them to the Rainbow where others could see it. There was a general feeling in the village that, if they were going to find out who had stolen the money,

tinder-box

tinder-box, box containing things that are needed for lighting a fire
pedlar, person who goes from place to place and house to house selling things

there was a great deal to be done at the Rainbow. No man needed to give his wife an excuse for going there to do his duty.

Silas Marner was sent for, so that he could answer 5 more questions. He too remembered the pedlar. But the man had gone on his way when Silas told him at the door that he wanted nothing. He had not been inside the cottage, and Silas could not remember what he had looked like.

10 This *annoyed* his listeners. For almost everyone else could now remember that the pedlar had an evil, *foreign* look about him, and that he had worn large rings in his ears.

If Master Marner were not so blind, Mr Snell later 15 remarked to Godfrey Cass, he would have seen the pedlar near his cottage. For of course he must have been hiding near the cottage, if he had forgotten his tinder-box in the ditch nearby. Godfrey, however, agreed with those who pointed out that the tinder-box might not 20 have belonged to the pedlar at all.

* * *

While his neighbours continued to argue during the days that followed, Silas tried to get on with his work. The loom was there, and the weaving, and the pattern in his cloth continued to grow.

25 But the bright *treasure* in the hole under his feet was gone. He had nothing to count in the evenings. It was

annoyed, feeling that someone or something is being a nuisance
foreign, not from those parts or from a different country
treasure, goods of great value or a much loved person

as though the last bit of light in his life had been put out. He moaned every now and then, as he sat weaving, making a sound like someone in pain.

In the evenings, he would sit in front of his fire with his head in his hands. He would moan then, long and low, like someone who did not want to be heard. Sometimes he would get up, open his door, and stand for a long time looking up the road or over at the Stone-pit. Not that he could see very far or very clearly. Yet he seemed to have a feeling that, if help were to come to him, it would come from outside.

Most of his neighbours were no longer quite so afraid of him. One or two could still be heard talking about Master Marner's magic cures, his secret ways, and the fact that he had not put a foot inside the church in all the years they had known him. That kind of person, some said, could lose their money in strange ways.

"That poor *creature*," most of the neighbours said, when they talked about the robbery at the cottage. Why, there was no reason to be afraid of Master Marner. The poor man had not even enough sense to hang on to his own money.

Everyone wanted to hear more details about the robbery and everyone hoped for more news. When Silas walked along the lanes or through the village these days, people would stop and greet him.

Mr Macey had called at the cottage to offer him the chance of a *Sunday suit* at a low price. "Then you can come to church and be a bit neighbourly," Mr Macey had said. Mrs Winthrop, the *wheelwright's* wife, known

creature, living thing - an animal or a person
Sunday suit, best set of clothes, used for church on Sundays
wheelwright, person who makes and mends wheels

to all as Dolly, had also been by to cheer him up. Silas, however, had not much to say to anyone.

Perhaps his life was beginning to take a new turn. But he himself only felt a sense of loss.

5 "I'll be back soon", Dolly had promised, "I'll do my Christmas baking and I'll bring my little boy, Aaron, to see you."

Silas had stood at his door and watched her go. Then he had got back into the seat of his loom and con-
10 tinued weaving, trying not to think of the empty hole beneath his feet.

4

On the afternoon following Mrs Osgood's party, Godfrey Cass stopped at the Rainbow for a drink on his way to Batherley. He had decided to ride over there himself
15 to find out whether the horse was sold or not. He could wait no longer.

But instead of a quiet drink, before getting on the road, he had to listen to old Mr Snell going on and on about a tinder-box. Godfrey could spare no more time
20 on all these details. He started out for Batherley as soon as he could.

Just a few miles outside Raveloe, he met Bryce.

"Well, Mr Godfrey, that's a lucky brother of yours, that Master Dunstan, isn't he?" had been Bryce's greet-
25 ing.

Godfrey did not know what he meant. But in a couple of minutes he had the whole story. His best and favourite horse, Wildfire, was dead. And Dunstan had not got a penny for him. No wonder that young broth-
30 er of his had been afraid to show himself at the Red House.

Bryce, in fact, had been on his way to Raveloe to make sure that Godfrey knew about Wildfire. He was afraid that Dunstan might have been trying to sell the horse without Godfrey's knowledge.

"But where can Dunstan be?" Bryce wanted to know. "We haven't seen him at Batherley. He couldn't have been hurt, because he walked off and left the horse."

"Hurt?" said Godfrey. "He certainly won't be hurt. He is the kind who only hurts other people. We'll hear from him soon enough, I expect."

Godfrey said goodbye to Bryce and turned around to make his way back to Raveloe. He needed to think things out. There was no longer any way out. The Squire still thought that Fowler had never paid up. He would have to be told everything. He, the eldest son, would be thrown out of his home. And the same would happen to Dunstan as soon as he turned up again at the Red House.

He must at least let his father know that the rent money had been collected. Perhaps he should first tell him about his own weakness - letting Dunstan have the rent money. Then he could go on to say that Dunstan had a hold over him, because of something that he himself had done.

Perhaps it would be best if his father were allowed to think that his eldest son had done something very bad. Then the old Squire might *be relieved* to hear that it was nothing worse than a foolish marriage. Why, he might even want to keep quiet about the marriage! Maybe he would prefer to keep his son at home, rather than have everyone in the countryside talking about their family.

Godfrey could see that it would be much better if he explained all this to his father himself. What if his wife, Molly, turned up at the Red House, as she had said she would, and told all to the Squire? He couldn't bear to think about it. He arrived home in the early evening with his mind made up. He would tell his father everything, after breakfast the next morning.

* * *

Godfrey had breakfast early the next day. It was a winter morning, dark and cold. He sat waiting for his younger brothers to finish their meal and be off. There was still no sign of Dunstan. But this was not unusual and nobody had talked about it.

Only Godfrey knew that Dunstan had good reason to keep away for a while. Probably he was off some-

be relieved, feel better, because a fear has gone away

where, *borrowing* from friends and drinking too much. He would not care about the trouble he was causing his older brother. Life would be the same as usual when he got back. That was the best he could hope for. If only he could settle this matter of the missing money with 5 his father.

The Squire appeared at this point, his dog at his heels, interrupting Godfrey's line of thought. He was a tall, large man of sixty with a deep voice.

"Not finished breakfast yet?" said the Squire. "Ring 10 the bell for my ale, will you?"

borrowing, taking something, promising to give it back

"Yes, sir, I have finished," said Godfrey, getting up to ring the bell, "I was waiting to speak to you."

His father began cutting slices of beef and giving bits to the dog. Godfrey waited until the ale had been brought and the door closed again. By that time, the dog had eaten enough beef to make a poor man's Christmas dinner.

"I've had a bit of bad luck with Wildfire," he began, "It happened the day before yesterday."

"What! Broke his knees?" said the Squire, taking a draft of ale. "Ha! so you want another horse, do you? Well, you can think again. I'm as short of *cash* as any old tramp. People will not pay their *debts*. That damned Fowler promised me a hundred last month. I'm sending a man out there this morning."

"It's worse than that. Wildfire has been staked and killed. I wasn't thinking of asking you to buy me another horse."

"What are you talking about, young man?" said the Squire, starting to get annoyed.

Godfrey tried again.

"Well, Dunstan took Wildfire to the hunt for me the other day to sell him. He made a bargain with Bryce for a hundred and twenty. But then he rode with the hounds and staked Wildfire. If it hadn't been for that, I would have paid you a hundred pounds this morning."

The Squire put down his knife and fork and stared at Godfrey in amazement. He could not imagine any reason in the world why his son should want to pay **him** a hundred pounds!

"I'm very sorry, sir. I am to blame," Godfrey went on.

cash, money that you have with you or can easily get
debts, money that is owed to someone else

Fowler did pay that hundred pounds. He paid it to me when I was over there last month. Dunstan asked me for it. And I let him have it, because I hoped I would be able to pay it back to you long before this."

The Squire was purple with anger, before his son had finished speaking. "What! The money was paid? And you let Dunstan have it. Are you turning out a *scamp*? Are you? I'll turn you both out of the house, I will. Why should you let him have the money? There is some lie at the bottom of this."

"There is no lie, sir," said Godfrey. "I would never spend the money on myself. Dunstan asked me for it. I was a fool and let him have it. That is the whole story."

"Go and get Dunstan in here at once. We'll get to the bottom of this. I'll turn him out. I said I would and I will. Go and get him."

Godfrey had to explain to his father that Dunstan was not back yet. No doubt he would be turning up again soon.

"And why should you let him have my money? Answer me that," said the Squire, getting angry at Godfrey again when Dunstan was not within reach. "I think you've been up to some trick," the Squire went on, "and you were paying Dunstan not to tell."

Godfrey felt his heart thump in fright, at this sudden guess.

"Why, sir, it was nothing at all. Just a bit of young men's *foolery*. A little matter between Dunstan and me - not worth bothering about," he said, in a weak voice.

"Fooleries! It is high time that you were finished with fooleries," the Squire went on. "Not so long ago

scamp, person who does tricks that are not honest
foolery, a silly thing to do, mainly done for fun

you seemed to be thinking of getting married. And did I make any difficulties, as some fathers would? Did I?"

"No, sir, you did not," said Godfrey, beginning to feel very hot and uncomfortable.

5 "Certainly, I did not. I'd be just as pleased to see you married to Lammeter's daughter as anybody. But you don't seem to know your mind well enough to make both your legs walk one way. Has she said that she won't have you?"

10 "No, sir, she has not." Godfrey felt even more uncomfortable. "But I don't think she will," he added.

"Think! Why, you haven't even the courage to ask her! I'll make the offer for you, you young fool. I'll talk to Lammeter about it."

15 This made Godfrey even more *alarmed*. "I'd rather let it be, please sir, just at present. She is not too pleased with me just now. I'd rather speak for myself and manage things on my own."

"Well, speak, then. Manage it, and *turn over a new* 20 *leaf*," replied the Squire.

"Yes, I'd rather let things be with the Lammeters just at the moment," said Godfrey. "I hope you won't try to hurry things on by saying anything?"

"I shall do what I choose," said the Squire. "I'll let 25 you know who is the master around here. Now go out to the yard and tell that man of mine to wait for me. He is not going over to Fowler's after all."

Godfrey left the room and did as he was asked. He had the rest of the day to wonder whether he was bet- 30 ter off or worse off than he had been before.

alarmed, suddenly fearful
turn over a new leaf, to make a new start or to begin behaving in a better way

The problem about Fowler's money had been dealt with. He had not been turned out of his home, yet. But what on earth could he do about Nancy Lammeter? The Christmas parties would be starting soon. And then there would be their own big dance at New Year. The Squire and Mr Lammeter would be seeing a lot of each other. Something would be said. What could he do? And what would Dunstan say, when he came home and heard that his father was waiting for an explanation?

* * *

Preparations for Christmas were also making themselves felt out at the cottage near the Stone-pit. Not that Silas Marner gave much thought to Christmas.

But others remembered his misfortune. Weeks had passed and still the Justice had not reported that any pedlar had been found. But small pieces of pork, *black puddings* and other tasty items were finding their way, from such houses as the Osgoods' and the Crackenthorps', out to Marner's cottage. Soon Dolly Winthrop was on her way there again.

One Sunday afternoon she took her little boy Aaron with her and went to call on Silas, carrying some small cakes. Seven-year-old Aaron had heard a lot about Master Marner from some of the older boys, who had been out at the cottage peeping in the window. He was scared stiff at the thought of going inside the cottage. Now he walked along beside his mother, dressed in his best Sunday clothes. He had been to church that day

black puddings, type of sausage

with his mother and father and all of his older brothers.

Aaron's round cheeks were like two polished red apples in the *frosty* weather. And the white *frill* he wore around his neck had been ironed so well, it looked like a plate for the apples. For Dolly Winthrop was an excellent housewife, who got up at half past four every morning to start her work. This left her plenty of time for helping out her neighbours, when help was needed. And Dolly was the first person everyone in Raveloe turned to for help whenever there was an illness or a death in the family.

Aaron was very frightened by the noise of the loom as they neared the cottage.

"Ah, it is as I thought," said Dolly, sadly.

They had to knock loudly before Silas could hear them. When he did come to the door, he opened it wide to let them in. He did not seem annoyed at having his work interrupted. But he did not seem pleased

frosty, very cold
frill, a strip of cloth; here: a collar

to see them either. He said nothing. He moved a chair a little, as a sign that Dolly was to sit down. Aaron immediately hid behind it.

"I did some baking yesterday, Master Marner, and the *lard*-cakes turned out better than usual," said Dolly. "If there is any good to be got in this world, we have need of it. And I hope they'll bring good to you, Master Marner."

"Thank you - thank you kindly," said Silas, putting down the cakes and sitting down himself. He did not seem to be able to think of anything else to say or do.

"Yes, if there is good anywhere, we have need of it," said Dolly again. "But you didn't hear the church bells this morning, Master Marner? The loom makes such a noise, I suppose, you can't hear the bells and you don't know that it's Sunday!"

"Yes, I did. I heard the bells," said Silas.

"Dear heart!" said Dolly, pausing to take this in. She did not know that there had been no bells at Lantern Yard. To Silas, the bells of Raveloe were only a noise, far away. He never thought of them as a sign that it was a day of rest, much less a day of prayer.

"But wouldn't it be lovely if you came to see the church at Christmas?" asked Dolly, suddenly getting a good idea. "You'd see the *holly* and the *yew* and the candles and hear the *hymns*. And you'd feel a great deal better. Do you know what I mean?"

"I know nothing about church," he said. "I've never been to church."

lard, melted fat from a pig
holly, *yew*, plants with red berries and leaves that are green all the year round, used for Christmas decoration (see picture, page 50)
hymns, songs of praise, usually sung in church

"No!" said Dolly, in a tone of wonder. "Maybe they had no church where you were born?"

"Yes, they had, many churches. It was a big town. But I went to chapel."

5 This was a word that Dolly didn't know. She did not like to ask, fearing that it might be something *wicked*.

"Well, if you've never been to church, there's no telling the good it'll do you," she said brightly after a moment's thought. "If a bit of trouble comes, I feel I 10 can put up with it, for I have the feeling that I've looked for help in the right place," she added, gently.

As she spoke, Aaron appeared around the side of his mother's chair. Silas seemed to notice him for the first time and offered him a cake.

15 "Oh! For shame, Aaron," said his mother, as he stretched out his hand. "You don't want cake again. Well, let me hold it for you then, while you sing the Christmas *carol* for Master Marner. He has a voice like a bird, Master Marner! Wait till you hear."

20 Aaron was at last persuaded to sing the hymn his father had taught him - "God Rest You, Merry Gentlemen."

"That's Christmas music," Dolly told Marner, when the carol was finished and Aaron had got his cake.

wicked, wrong, evil or bad
carol, song of joy, sung especially at Christmas time

"Yes," said Silas "very pretty." He had found it very strange, a song with a sound like a hammer at work, not a bit like any of the hymns he had known in the old days.

Dolly seemed to think that it was time to go home. Silas said, "Goodbye and thank you kindly," as he opened the door for them. He knew that she was a good woman. But he felt pleased that they were going and that he could get back to his weaving.

And so, Silas did not do as his neighbours had suggested. He did not go to church. He spent his Christmas Day alone. He ate some meat that he had been given as a present. He opened his door to look out at the hard frost that seemed to press on every blade of grass. Later, when it began snowing again, he sat at his fire, his head between his hands. It was the cold that told him the day had passed, and that his fire had gone out.

In Raveloe village, the bells had rung merrily. There were more people in the church that day than all the rest of the year. Mrs Kimble, the Squire's sister, and her husband, the doctor, came to the family party at the Red House on Christmas Day.

None of the family mentioned the fact that Dunstan was not there. Nobody felt sorry about it, certainly not Godfrey. And nobody seemed to fear that he would stay away too long. Not once, during the last six weeks, had Godfrey thought that Dunstan's *absence* from home could have anything to do with the robbery out at the Stone-pit. The idea that one of the Cass family would do such a thing had never entered his head.

When the family had all finished their hearty

absence, not being in the place where one is expected to be

Christmas dinner, they sat with their drinks at the fire. The really big party at the Red House would be the dance at New Year. Everyone for miles around would be coming.

5

People had been arriving for the New Year party at the Red House since early morning. By late afternoon the house was buzzing with activity in every room. There was so much food in the kitchen, it looked as though an army was coming to dine. And many hands were busy preparing more food.

Extra feather beds had been put down on the floors of all the bedrooms. For this was a party that began with a dance on New Year's Eve and would last for several days. The snow had begun to fall again in the early afternoon, beginning to cover the icy puddles on the roads. Everyone with any distance to travel hoped to arrive before the weather got any worse.

The Lammeter sisters, Nancy and Priscilla, were

changing into their party dresses in a bedroom that was to be shared by no less than six ladies. Since five of the ladies were in the room, and a lot of the floor covered in beds, there was not much space to move about. The two Miss Gunns were there, daughters of the *wine merchant* from Lytherly, already dressed in the height of fashion. A *queue* had formed at the *looking-glass*.

"After you," Miss Ladbrook was saying to Priscilla, who was waiting to take her turn.

"Thanks ever so much. I won't be a minute," said Priscilla, who did not care very much what the result was like when she was dressed in her finest clothes.

"Oh! Doesn't this grey silk make my skin look as yellow as butter!" she said, as she put on her eardrops in far less than a minute. "Well, I **am** *ugly* and that's the truth. But I don't mind a bit, do you?" she said brightly, turning to the Miss Gunns. "The pretty ones like Nancy keep the men off us. And that suits me perfectly well. Now, where did I put my *coral* necklace?"

Nobody seemed to have any reply to these remarks. And within a very short time the Miss Gunns, followed by Miss Ladbrook, had gone downstairs, leaving the Lammeter sisters to help each other with their necklaces. Nancy had time to explain to Priscilla that she had better try to be more polite to the Miss Gunns, who had not liked her remarks. And Priscilla, who was five years older than her young sister, had time to give a bit of her own advice.

wine merchant, person who buys wine in large quantities and sells it to shop-keepers and others
queue, line of people
looking-glass, mirror in which one can see oneself
ugly, not pleasant or pretty to look at
coral, pink-coloured stone, madefrom the bones of sea animals

"Now let us see if there are any nice young gentlemen here, Nancy. I've no patience with you - sitting on an *addled* egg for ever, as if there was never a fresh one in the world. You'll never change that Master Godfrey, you know."

"Don't talk so, Prissy," said Nancy, blushing, and turning away from her sister to hide the fact. "You know that I don't intend to get married, ever."

"Nonsense," replied Priscilla, as the two sisters left the room, ready to go down to their tea.

But Nancy had meant what she said. She believed that a true and pure woman only really loves one man in her lifetime. It was her misfortune that Godfrey was not turning out the way that she had hoped. When she had first discovered that she loved him, she had thought him such a fine person. As it turned out, he treated her quite badly at times - *paying* her all kinds of *attentions* one minute and then *ignoring* her for long periods of time in between. It was very painful, especially when other people remarked upon it. Nothing, she felt, could persuade her to marry a man who acted like that.

The sisters came down the stairs together. They were dressed completely alike, so that everyone could see they were sisters, and yet they looked so very different. Priscilla rushed as fast as she could, looking much as she had described herself, thinking of her tea. Nancy stepped with the neatness of a little bird, looking like a picture in her silvery silk and white lace, thinking of

addled, an addled egg is one that is not good; an addled person is mixed-up or confused
paying attentions, talking, listening, dancing, etc.
ignoring, acting as though the other person is not there

what she had just said to Priscilla. Her little coral necklace and eardrops seemed to match the slight blush on her cheek.

"Ah! Here comes Miss Nancy," said Mr Crackenthorp, who was standing in the hall. "If anyone complains that it is a hard winter, I'll be able to tell them that I saw roses blooming on New Year's Eve - eh, Godfrey, what do you say? On Miss Nancy's cheek, eh?"

"Better hurry, Godfrey, if you want to make sure that Miss Nancy keeps the first dance for you," added the Squire, who was passing through on his way to the parlour.

The kind of remarks that Godfrey dreaded, and that Nancy sometimes found painful, seemed to be all around them even before they reached their afternoon tea.

* * *

While Godfrey was showing Nancy to her place at the laden table in the Red House, his wife, unknown to him, was not so many miles away. She was walking with slow steps through the freezing, snow-covered lanes, just a few miles from Raveloe. She was carrying her sleeping child in her arms.

This was a trip that Molly had planned for a long time. The idea had come to her when Godfrey, in anger, had told her that he would rather die than *acknowledge* her as his wife. From that day, she had planned to turn up at the Red House in the middle of the Squire's famous party.

She would walk in, wearing her oldest *rags*. And in front of as many people as possible, she would present herself and her baby as the wife and child of the Squire's eldest son. The thought of seeing their faces had made her smile every time she thought of it, for months past.

Molly knew very well that there was a reason why she lived in such poor *lodgings*, and why even the best of her clothes were in very bad condition. It was not that her husband gave her very little money. The reason was that she spent almost all the money she could get on opium.

She had set out from Batherly at an early hour, her last *phial* of opium tucked carefully into her dress, and her baby held tightly in her arms. Godfrey was rich. Molly held on to the idea that, as soon as she was

acknowledge, here: accept or recognize another person in a public way
rags, very old clothes that are torn and need to be mended
lodgings, rooms for living in, for which money is paid
phial, small glass bottle, usually used for medicine

acknowledged as his wife, she would be rich too.

When the snow had begun to fall more heavily, she had waited some time for it to stop. But she had waited in the shelter of the warm shed longer than she knew. It was nearly seven o'clock in the evening now, and her arms were aching from the effort of carrying her child. Fortunately, the child had stopped crying and had fallen asleep again. Molly was tired out trying to pick her way around the icy patches and feeling her way along the hedge. The little starlight there had been earlier was now clouded over. Her feet were wet and a freezing wind had come up.

Had she known these lanes better, she might have been glad to know that she was not very far from Raveloe. But she was not sure how much further she had to go. She was feeling so cold and tired that even the thought of the surprised faces at the Red House did not make her smile now. There was only one source of help that she knew. Her hand went to the phial.

The weight of the child, held for a moment on one arm, reminded her that it would be better if she could reach the village first. Then there would be other people nearby. But she must be very nearly there by now. She put something to her lips and threw it away. It was the empty phial that she threw over the hedge.

She walked on, feeling once again that everything would soon be better. Her feet moved more and more slowly. But she was not aware of this. It was not long before she had only one thought in her head - the need to lie down and sleep.

Molly had reached a point in the lane where she could no longer feel the hedge brushing her leg and arm. After a few more steps she came to a small *furze* bush. She sank down against it, resting her head on the bush, still holding on to her little child. Soon, she was aware of nothing at all. Her arms no longer held the child tightly to her.

There was a little cry of "*mammy*", as the child rolled down to its mother's knees, its blue eyes open wide. Its pillow seemed to have slipped backwards, and further cries of "mammy" brought no *response* at all. There was a bright light dancing on the white ground. The child held out her hand to catch the light. But it could not be caught in that way. It held up its head to see where the light came from. It came from a very bright place. The child began to *toddle* through the snow towards the bright light.

The dirty old blanket was left behind, and the little *bonnet* bobbed up and down on its back as it toddled on

furze, small bush with green leaves all the year round
"*mammy*", child's name for its mother
response, a word or action given in answer to the word or action of another person
toddle, a little child's walk with short uncertain steps
bonnet, here: hat with strings that tie under the chin

to the open door of Silas Marner's cottage. In it went, right up to the lovely warm fire. There was a nice dry sack, ready to lie on, in front of the fire.

Silas stamped the snow off his boots in the doorway and came into the cottage carrying a heavy basket of logs. He was just about to put down the basket when, suddenly, he stopped.

There was gold on the floor in front of the fire. His own gold had been brought back to him! He put down the basket. But for a few moments he was unable to reach out and grasp his treasure. Then he stretched out his hand for the coins. But his fingers found soft warm curls.

Silas fell on his knees and bent his head low to see this amazing sight more closely. It was a sleeping child - a round fair thing with soft yellow rings all over its head. Could this be his little sister come back to him in a dream? The little sister whom he had carried about when he was a small boy for a year before she died? **Was** it a dream? Certainly, he had stood in a dream-like state for a long time at the open door tonight. But this was no dream. He felt the curls once more.

There was a little cry. The child was awake. He lifted it onto his knee to stop the crying. It put its arms around his neck but began crying louder. "Mammy," it said, crying at the same time. "Hush, now, hush, everything is fine," said Silas, patting it on the back and rocking himself and the baby back and forth gently. He would try giving it some of his *porridge*, which had got cool by the side of the fire.

He had plenty to do during the next hour. The por-

porridge, soft food, made by boiling oats in water

ridge was warmed up a little and made sweeter with some dry brown sugar. This soon stopped the cries of the little one. She lifted her blue eyes with a wide quiet stare at Silas as he put the spoon into her mouth. When she had had enough to eat, she slipped from his knee and began to toddle about.

Silas jumped up to follow after her, afraid that she might fall and hurt herself. But then she sat on the floor and began to pull at her boots. She looked up at Silas with a crying face, as if the boots hurt her.

He got the boots off with some difficulty. Then the little one immediately began playing with her toes, finding this the greatest of fun. Silas was beginning to smile at all this enjoyment when he realised that the boots were wet. The child had been walking in the snow. Well, of course it had got here somehow! He had not been thinking clearly.

He lifted her up in his arms and went to the door. As he opened it, she cried "mammy" once more, which Silas had not heard since she first woke up. Bending down, he could see little foot marks in the snow.

Following these, he soon came to the furze bush. "Mammy, mammy," the little one cried again, trying to escape from his arms and slip to the ground. Silas could see that there was more than a bush before him. There was a human body, the head sunk low in the bush and half covered with shaken snow.

* * *

It was the early supper time at the Red House. The Squire was taking a pause from playing cards. He had just gone around patting his visitors on the back and making the amusing remarks that he felt a Squire should make. And now he joined a small group, seated near the card tables, among whom sat Nancy. Godfrey Cass stood in a corner from which he could see Nancy. He had no wish to join the group, fearing that his father would immediately start to make remarks about Nancy and himself. Lifting his eyes from a long look at Nancy, he suddenly saw the strangest sight he had ever seen in his life.

It was his own child carried in Silas Marner's arms. Of course he could not be sure, not having seen the child for months. There must be some hope that he was mistaken.

Seeing that Mr Crackenthorp and Mr Lammeter were already on their way over to stop Silas from coming further into the room, he immediately went to join them. He must hear every word. He did his best to control himself, aware that anyone might wonder why he was white-lipped and trembling.

By now, all eyes at that end of the room were on Silas Marner. The Squire himself was rising from his chair.

"What's this? What are you doing, coming in here in this way?"

"I've come for the doctor - I want the doctor," Silas had said, in the first moment, to Mr Crackenthorp.

"Why, what's the matter, Marner?" Mr Crackenthorp had replied. "The doctor is here. Just say quietly what you want him for."

"It's a woman," said Silas, speaking low, just as Godfrey came up. "She's dead, I think - dead in the snow at the Stone-pit - not far from my door."

"Hush! Go out into the hall there. I'll find the doctor for you," said Mr Crackenthorp, turning round to look for Kimble. "Found a woman in the snow - and thinks she's dead," he added in a quiet voice to the Squire. "Let's not shock the ladies. Just tell them a poor woman is ill from cold and hunger. I'll find Kimble."

"What child is it?" several ladies wanted to know. Among them was Nancy, who was also making her way across the room.

"Some poor woman has been found in the snow, I believe," was the answer Godfrey gave. (After all, **am** I certain? he asked himself silently.)

"Why, you'd better leave the child here, then, Master Marner," said Mrs Kimble. But she made no move to bring the small dirty clothes into contact with her own *satin* dress. "I'll tell one of the girls to fetch it."

"No, no - I can't part with it, I can't let it go," said Silas. "It's come to me - I've a right to keep it."

He had not given a thought to the matter until the suggestion was made to take her away from him. Then he found that the idea *horrified* him.

"Have you ever heard the like?" said Mrs Kimble with a smile to the lady beside her.

"Now, ladies, I must trouble you to stand aside," said Dr Kimble. "Get me a pair of thick boots, Godfrey, will you? And let somebody run up to Winthrop's and fetch Dolly. She's the best woman to get."

They made their way into the hall, where Godfrey soon found a suitable pair of boots for Kimble. The baby had begun crying again, sorry to be leaving the bright lights and smiling faces. "Mammy," she cried, holding on to Marner as tightly as she could. Godfrey

satin, shiny smooth cloth, used for party dresses
horrified, very frightened or shocked

wanted to get out of this awful situation as soon as possible.

"I'll go and fetch the Winthrop woman," he said, taking his hat and coat and leaving the house as quickly as he could.

In a few minutes he was on his way out to the Stonepit by the side of Dolly. He offered to wait outside when they came to the cottage, in case there was anything to be fetched from the doctor's house.

"Well, sir, you've a very good heart," said Dolly. "Just look in at the Rainbow and ask my husband to come instead, if you want to get back."

But Godfrey waited outside the door of the cottage, walking back and forth in the snow. The terror in his mind was that the woman might **not** be dead. If only she was dead, he would be a good fellow in the future, he told himself. The child would be looked after somehow. I may even marry Nancy, he thought to himself. If, on the other hand, Molly was alive, that would be the end of everything for him.

Godfrey never knew how long it was before the door opened and Dr Kimble came out.

"What nonsense for you to come out. Why didn't you send for one of the men? There's nothing to be done. She's been dead for hours."

"What sort of woman is she?" Godfrey wanted to know.

"Young, long black hair, worn out. Some tramp - quite in rags. She's got a wedding-ring though. They must take her body to the *workhouse* tomorrow. Come along."

workhouse, place to which very poor people were sent, usually to work or be cared for

"I want to look at her," said Godfrey. "I think I saw a woman like that yesterday. I'll catch up with you in a minute or two."

For the first time in his life, Godfrey entered Silas Marner's cottage. One glance at the dead face on the pillow was enough. He remembered every detail of that face, smoothed and cared for now by Dolly. Sixteen years later, when he was to tell the full story of this night for the first time, he could remember quite clearly the face of the wife that he had hated.

Looking towards the fire, he could see the small hand of his child pulling Marner's cheek. The wide-open blue eyes looked up at him without any sign of *recognition*. His feelings were strangely mixed. His daughter was a lovely girl. He felt quite proud of her. At the same time, he need have no fear that she knew who he was.

"Will you take the child *to the parish* tomorrow?" he asked, trying to sound as though he didn't much mind what happened.

"Who says so?" said Marner. "Will they make me?"

"Why, you wouldn't want to keep her, would you?"

"Unless anyone shows that they have a right to take her away from me. She's a *lone* thing. The mother's dead. And I'm a lone thing," said Silas.

"Poor little thing. Let me give something towards buying it clothes."

Godfrey gave Silas a half-guinea that he had in his pocket and hurried out of the cottage to catch up with

recognition, knowing someone again that has been seen before
to the parish, to the local church (and probably from there to the work-house)
lone, on one's own, without other people

Kimble. Thoughts were racing through his mind. Now he would be able to promise Nancy and himself that he would always be just the kind of man she wanted him to be. On he ran. Dunstan might tell the story when he came back. But with the help of some money, he would keep his mouth shut. As for the child, he would see that it was cared for. There was Kimble now.

"Not the same woman I saw yesterday," he gasped, as he caught up with Dr Kimble.

"Just as well I got out of the house though. It was my turn to dance with the other Miss Gunn," he added, as the two men made their way back through the snow to the party at the Red House.

6

There was a *pauper's burial* that week in Raveloe. Up at Kench Yard at Batherley it was known that the dark-haired woman with the fair child had gone away again.

Silas Marner's decision to keep "the tramp's child" had become the talk of the village, just as the robbery of his money had been months before. How would a lone man manage with a child that was barely two years old? The women were ready to offer all kinds of suggestions.

But Dolly Winthrop was the one that Silas asked for help. He had shown her the half-guinea that Godfrey had given him, and asked what he should do about getting some clothes for the child.

"Eh, Master Marner, the only thing you need to buy is a pair of shoes," said Dolly. "I've got all the little things Aaron wore five years ago. Don't spend your

pauper's burial, funeral held for a person who had no money

money on baby-clothes. At that age they grow like the grass in May."

And that same day Dolly had brought her *bundle* and explained to Marner, one by one, what each tiny *garment* was for. 5

"The angels in heaven couldn't be prettier," said Dolly, as she sat rubbing the little one's curls, having given her a bath. "Someone was taking care of it. And brought it to your door, Master Marner," she went on. "Yes, it walked in over the snow just like a little *starved robin*. Didn't you say the door was open?" 10

"Yes," said Silas. "Yes, the door was open. The money is gone I don't know where, and this is come from I don't know where."

"Ah," said Dolly, "all the big things come and go with no effort of ours. That they do - night and morning, rain and sun. One goes and the other comes. We don't know how or where. I think you are right to keep the little one, Master Marner - seeing that it has been sent to you." 15 20

Baby was having her toes dried on Dolly's knee. "Gug-gug-gug," she said, finding this quite as much fun as playing with her toes herself.

"I'll come and see to the child for you any day," said Dolly. "And I can wash her few little things with one hand when I have my *suds* about me." 25

"Thank you ... kindly," said Silas, slowly. "I'll be very glad if you tell me things." He moved his chair closer

bundle, things collected together
garment, any piece of clothing worn on the body
starved robin, small bird unable to find food that often hops up to the doors of country cottages in winter time
suds, soapy water

to Dolly and the baby.

"But I want to do things for it myself," he went on. "Otherwise it might get fond of somebody else and not fond of me - I can learn, I can learn."

"Eh, to be sure. I've seen men that are very handy with children," said Dolly, gently. "Now, you see this goes first, next to the skin," she went on, lifting up a little shirt and putting it on.

"Yes," said Silas, leaning over to look more closely and make quite sure which garment it was. Baby immediately put both small arms around his head. "Gug-gug-gug," she said.

"See there," said Dolly, "she's fondest of you. You take her on your lap, Master Marner. You put the things on. And then you can say that you've looked after her from the first."

Silas took the little one on his knee and the clothes from Dolly and put them on, one after the other. Dolly told him what to do, while Baby did everything to make it as difficult as possible. At last it was done.

"There, then, you take to it quite easily, Master Marner," said Dolly. "But what are you going to do when you have to work?"

They both thought about this for a while. They walked around the loom, Dolly pointing out the need to keep the sharp things, like the *scissors*, out of Baby's reach. At last, Silas came up with the idea that he

scissors

would tie a long strip of something to one leg of the loom. The other end could be fastened to the little one, so that she would be able to toddle about and play. Dolly thought this might work. She had four boys herself, but was inclined to think that a girl might play more happily than a boy. She would bring a little chair and some red rags for her to play with.

"And when she gets old enough, Master Marner, I can teach her to *knit* and mend and everything!" said Dolly, happily.

"But she'll be **my** little one," Marner said quickly. "She'll be nobody else's."

"No, to be sure. You'll have a right to her. If you are a father to her and do everything for her that a good father should."

Dolly felt that this was the moment to bring up something that was of the most extreme importance. Baby would have to be *christened* and brought to church, just like other people's children. When the point was made, however, Silas became very anxious. He did not know what she meant, having only heard of *baptism*. And he had only seen the baptism of grown men and women.

"What is it you mean by **christened**?" he said at last, "won't folks be good to her without it?"

"Master Marner, did you have no father and mother to teach you to say your prayers and such like?" Dolly was very shocked.

Silas had to explain that of course he had had par-

knit, to make things from wool using a pair of needles
christen(ed), giving a baby a name during baptism
baptism, rite (ceremony) of the christian church during which a person, usually a baby, becomes a member of the church

ents who had taught him the right things. But they were the right things in that place, a long way from Raveloe. He wanted to do every single thing that was right for the little one in this part of the world. She had only to tell him.

It was soon agreed that she would speak to Mr Macey and Mr Crackenthorp about the christening. The next problem was to decide upon a name.

"My mother's name was Hephzibah," said Silas, "and my little sister was called after her. It's a *Bible* name."

"Then of course it must be a good name," said Dolly doubtfully. She was surprised Silas knew a strange name like that from the Bible.

"But it was awkward calling your little sister by such a hard name, when you'd nothing big to say, wasn't it, Master Marner?" was Dolly's further comment.

"We called her Eppie," said Silas.

And so the little girl who had toddled up to Silas' hearth on New Year's Eve was christened, and called Eppie. A double baptism was held in the church. Silas had made himself as clean and tidy as he could and Eppie had been dressed with special care. If Silas had been able to say what he felt, he would probably have said that the child had come to replace the gold. He was going to look after Eppie with infinitely more care than he had looked after his guineas.

The guineas had kept him at his loom, weaving longer and longer and keeping him away from other people. But Eppie got him away from his loom, bit by bit. As the weeks grew into months, he could be seen, even in the middle of the day, holding her by the hand,

bible, the books of the old and new testaments in the Christian church

walking along the lanes and looking at the flowers that grew there. People stopped to speak to them, with open faces and cheerful questions. Even the children were not afraid of him when Eppie was there.

When the sunshine grew strong and lasting, Silas could be seen carrying Eppie beyond the Stone-pit over to the Osgoods' meadow, where the buttercups grew. He would sit in the sun while Eppie picked flowers. "*Dad-dad*"," she would say, bringing him flowers. Then she would turn her ear to some sudden bird note. Silas would flap his arms and make signs of *hushed* stillness. They would listen for the note to come again. When it came, Eppie would laugh, clap her hands and try to jump up and down.

It was not long before Silas began to look for herbs again. While Eppie was busy learning new things, he seemed to be remembering more and more from his past.

Sometimes she kept him very busy indeed. By the time she was three years old, it was not always easy to keep an eye on her. She seemed to be learning new tricks every day. Dolly thought that there was only one way to deal with this. Eppie must be given a *smack* now and then.

"It's good for her. She has to learn, Master Marner. Only a good smack in a soft safe place will teach her."

But Silas could not bring himself to punish Eppie. And Dolly had to admit that she herself had never been very good about smacking her youngest son, Aaron. One day, however, he had been so bold that she

"dad-dad", or daddy, names which a child calls its father
hush(ed), to make a sign or sound that calls for silence
smack, slap or hit, lightly given with an open hand

had shut him up in the *coal-hole* for a minute. And that had taught him a lesson. Silas was strongly advised to think about this possibility.

It was not many days later that he had good reason to remember this bit of advice. He was busy at his loom, setting up a new piece of work and cutting off end pieces of twine with a click of his scissors. Eppie had been watching him for a while and had then gone over to play with some bits on her little bed. The broad piece of linen that was tied as a belt around her waist at one end, and to the leg of the loom at the other end, was plenty long enough to stretch that far.

When the noise of the weaving began, Eppie crept over as quietly as a mouse, got hold of the scissors, and crept back to the bed again. She had a good idea of what it could do. In a few minutes, she had cut through

coal-hole, place where coal for the fire is kept

the linen strip and had run outside into the sun.

Poor Silas had thought that she was a better child than usual that morning. It was not until he reached out for his scissors, and then looked up, that he realised what had happened. Eppie had run out by herself. Perhaps she had fallen into the Stone-pit! He ran from the house to the edge of the pit, calling "Eppie!", and looking everywhere. How long had she been out? "Eppie," he called again, as he looked with questioning *dread* at the smooth red surface of the water.

There was one hope - that she had gone as far as the Osgoods' meadow, where they often took their walks. The grass had got very tall, and Silas could see no sign of her. With dying hope, he went on to the next field where there was a little shallow pond. And there sat Eppie, in the middle of the mud, chatting to her own small boot. She had pulled off the boot to use as a bucket. She was happily filling up a *hoof-mark* at the edge of the dark green mud with water.

Silas was so full of joy when he saw his treasure again, that he lifted her up and half covered her with kisses. It was only as he carried her home, that he remembered the need to punish her. She must remember not to do this again.

"Naughty Eppie," he began, when he was home once more, with the child on his knee, pointing at her muddy feet and clothes. "Naughty to cut with the scissors and run away. Daddy must put Eppie in the coal-hole for being naughty!"

He half expected that this would make her cry. But

dread, fear felt very strongly
hoof-mark, small hole made by the foot of an animal

she clapped her hands and seemed quite pleased. He would have to show her that he really meant what he said.

He put her in the coal-hole, a dark and dirty cupboard beside the fire, and held the door closed. He had a horrible feeling that this was a strong measure of punishment indeed. In a moment there came a little cry, "Opy, opy!". Silas let her out again, saying, "Now Eppie will never be naughty again. Else she must go into the coal-hole - a black naughty place."

There was no more weaving done for the next hour. Eppie had to be washed and have clean clothes on. When that was done, Silas turned his attention to the linen strip that had been cut through. Perhaps he would not need it the rest of that morning. Surely the punishment would work that long. Though it might have been better if she had cried more. He was just about to place her little chair beside the loom, when she peeped out at him again with black hands and face, and said, "Eppie in *de toal-hole*!"

Silas gave up his belief in punishment after that. "She thinks it is all for fun, unless I hurt her. And I can't do that," he told Dolly later. "If she makes a bit of trouble, I can put up with it, Mrs Winthrop. And the only tricks she has are ones she'll grow out of." And so that was the end of punishments in the stone cottage.

It was difficult for Silas to have Eppie with him, carrying his yarn or linen at the same time, when he made his trips to the farm houses outside of Raveloe. But he did it, when it was at all possible. Only when he had a very long trip did he leave her at Dolly's house to play

de toal-hole, the coal-hole, said in a baby's way

with Aaron and his puppy dogs. It was not long before little curly-headed Eppie, the weaver's child, was known at many of the farm houses as well as in the village.

Everywhere he went, Silas was asked to sit a little and talk about the child. It was as though he had become a person whose joys and problems could be understood. "You'll be lucky, Master Marner if she takes the *measles* soon and easy," one would say to him. "There aren't many lone men that would take up with one as little as that," was a view that he heard often.

"Maybe it's the weaving that makes you as handy as a woman," an old lady said to him one day, "for weaving comes next to *spinning*. And then, if she turns out well, you'll have someone to look after you when you're helpless yourself," she went on, nodding as she spoke to show that she felt her own words to be true.

measles, illness common among children
spinning, making yarn or thread, usually women's work

Eppie, meanwhile, would be outside with the young people of the household - looking at the chickens, or trying to shake fruit off the trees in the *orchard*. She had become the link between Silas and the world
5 around him. These days, when he delivered his linen and earned his money, the guineas had a purpose beyond the money itself. Silas no longer had a treasure of coins. He had Eppie.

orchard, place in which many fruit trees grow

PART TWO

7

It was a bright autumn Sunday, sixteen years after Silas Marner had found his new treasure on the hearth in front of his fire. The morning service in the old Raveloe church had just ended. The bells were ringing cheerfully as people left the church. 5

The first couple to leave were Mr and Mrs Godfrey Cass. They were followed closely by a tall, elderly man and a younger middle-aged woman. The woman was Nancy's sister, Priscilla, who held her father's arm as they made their way slowly down the steps of the church. Nancy turned to them and pointed to a small narrow path that led through the churchyard to the road just opposite the Red House. They would go home that way, for Mr Lammeter and Priscilla had been invited to lunch at the Red House that day. 10 15

The old Squire had died several years earlier. For some reason, his title seemed to have died with him. Although Godfrey and Nancy were still the most important people in the village, people called them Mr and Mrs Cass, rather than the Squire and his wife. But it was still the custom in those parts that the more important people should be allowed to leave the church first. As they made their way down the little path through the churchyard, the steps outside the church began to fill up. 20 25

People were greeting each other, discussing the weather and starting to make their way home to their Sunday lunch. It was some time before Silas Marner could be seen, walking slowly towards the lane that led out to the Stone-pit. 30

With his bent shoulders and white hair, he still

looked older than his years. Beside him was a pretty girl of eighteen, tucking her long curly red-gold hair into her bonnet, as she walked along chatting to him. Eppie was admiring the colour of a *mountain-ash* that hung over the wall of the Rectory, and telling her father that what she wanted, more than anything, was to have a little garden.

"We could have *daisies* in it, Daddy, like Mrs Winthrop's," said Eppie. "But it might be too much hard work. There would be a lot of digging at the start."

mountain-ash, bush with white flowers and red berries
daisies, white flowers with yellow centres

"I can do the digging, child, if you want a bit of a garden. I can take a turn with a spade before I sit at my loom in the mornings. And the evenings are still long enough for a bit of digging."

"I can dig it for you, Master Marner," said a young man who had appeared by Eppie's side. 5

"Eh, Aaron, my lad, is that you?" said Silas. "I didn't see you. When Eppie is talking of things, I see nothing but what she is saying. Well," he went on, "if you help with the digging, we could get her a bit of a garden all 10 the sooner."

It was agreed, as they walked along, that they would all three start to plan the garden. Aaron worked as a gardener at some of the big houses, and he knew that a lot of plants were thrown on the *dump*. He could easily 15 bring cuttings of the plants and flowers that Eppie wanted.

"Can you bring your mother with you this afternoon, Aaron?" asked Eppie. "I wouldn't like to plan the garden without her knowing everything from the start - 20 would you, Father?"

"Yes, bring her if you can, Aaron. She is sure to have a word to say that will help us go about it the right way."

Aaron turned back towards the village, while Silas 25 and Eppie went on up the lane towards the Stone-pit.

"Daddy," she began, squeezing Silas's arm when they were on their own once more, "I'm so glad. There is nothing that I'd like more than a little garden. I knew Aaron would dig it for us." Then she added in a whis- 30 per, with a little laugh, "I knew that very well!"

dump, here: the part of the garden where unwanted plants are thrown to rot away

"You're a deep little one, you are. Here, let me carry your prayer-book. It'll fall with all that laughing and hopping about."

There was the sound of a sharp bark, as Eppie turned the key in the door of the cottage. This was the start of an excited welcome from Snap, the *terrier*, who ran around their legs, delighted that they were home again. A large sleepy cat sat sunning herself in the window, while her little kitten ran under the loom to hide from all the noise. But all this happy animal life was not the only change that had been made at the old stone cottage.

There was no bed now in the living room. Extra rooms had been built on. Everything was bright and clean enough to satisfy even Dolly Winthrop's eye. There was a fine oak table and three-cornered oaken chairs - not the kind of *furniture* that was usually to be seen in a poor cottage. They had come, with the beds and other things, from the Red House. For Mr Cass, as everyone said in the village, had been very kind to the old weaver through the years.

And, indeed, this was felt to be nothing but right. A man who had brought up an *orphan* child, and been father and mother to it, should be helped by those who could *afford* it. And Marner had lost all his money too. He only had what he worked for, week by week. And the weaving was not what it had been, for there had been less and less flax spun in Raveloe during the last ten years. Mr Macey, who was now an old man, eighty-

terrier, small dog, often used for hunting
furniture, chairs, tables, beds and such items in a house
orphan, child whose mother and father are dead or unknown
(to) afford, to have enough money to pay for things

six years old, had even been heard to say that when a man has done what Silas Marner had done, it was a sign that his money would come to light again. For that would be what was right.

Silas and Eppie sat and ate a potato pie for their lunch. It had been left to warm slowly, in safe Sunday fashion, in a dry pot over a dying fire.

"You go out into the sunshine, Daddy, and smoke your pipe," said Eppie, when they had finished eating. "I won't be long. I'll just clear away first, so the house will be nice and tidy when *godmother* comes."

5 Silas had begun smoking a pipe every day, a few years earlier. This, he had been told, would be good for him. It was as well to try what could do no harm, was the way the old Dr Kimble had put the matter. Silas did not enjoy the pipe very much. But he had got used to doing
10 everything that others thought was good and right, ever since he had found Eppie. And in this way, he had slowly learned the customs and beliefs that were the way of life of the people of Raveloe.

There had been many times when he had compared
15 this way of life with what he could remember from his past. Gradually, through the years, his memories had been awakened. He had begun to think that what had happened to him at Lantern Yard when he was a young man must have been the result of some mistake. It had
20 become easier for him to open his mind to Dolly and to tell her, bits at a time, all that he could remember of his early life.

It had been slow and difficult. Silas was not the best at explaining himself, and Dolly did not always under-
25 stand what he tried to tell.

At last, he had come to the worst part of his sad story, the part about the drawing of lots and what had happened afterwards. Dolly had shaken her head when she heard this part, and she had asked to hear it again many
30 times.

godmother, woman who makes the promises for a baby during baptism

"And you had the same Bible, you're sure of that, Master Marner? Is it the same as the one at church, the one Eppie is learning to read in?"

"Yes," said Silas, "every bit the same. And there is a drawing of lots in the Bible, mind you," he added. 5

"Oh dear, dear," said Dolly, sounding as though she had just heard a bad report about a person who was very sick.

"The rector knows how it all is, I'm sure. But it takes big words just to tell him things and I don't really know 10 the meaning of the good words that he says in the church. I only know that they are good words."

At some point, however, Dolly had learned very well what it was that Silas had on his mind. "It's this, Master Marner," she had said one day, "that if Them above 15 had done the right thing by you, They'd never have let you be turned out for a wicked thief, when you were innocent all the time."

"Ah!" said Silas, who had now come to understand that when Dolly talked of "Them", she was talking 20 about God, "that is what fell on me like a red-hot iron. Because, you see, then there was nobody that cared for me, *above* or *below*. Not even William, who had been my friend since we were lads."

"Eh, but he was a bad one. I don't suppose there is 25 another one like him in the whole world." Dolly wanted to think about it all a bit more. Sometimes when she was washing, or sitting still by the bed of a sick person, her thoughts became clearer to her, she felt.

"Master Marner," she said one day, when she had 30 come with Eppie's washing, " I think it's clear to me

above, *below*, here: in heaven, on earth

now. I just don't know if I can *bring it to my tongue's end.*"

Dolly had been sitting up with Bessy Fawkes, who had since died, leaving her young children behind her.

5 "It always comes to me when I'm sorry for *folks* and there is nothing in my power that I can do to help them."

"Yes, Mrs Winthrop?"

"It comes into my head, that Them above have a

10 much softer heart than the one I've got. I can't be any better than Them that made me, after all. And if anything looks hard to me, it can only be because there are things that I don't know."

"Yes, there's little enough we know, Mrs Winthrop."

15 "Them that made us know more than we do, Master Marner. I think that we have to do the right thing as far as we know, and then just trust."

"Trust, eh?"

"Yes, that's it. If *us that knows* so little can see a bit

20 of good and rights, then there must be a lot of good and rights bigger than we can know. I feel in my inside that it must be so. If you could have gone on trusting, Master Marner, you wouldn't have run away and been so alone."

25 "Ah, but that would have been hard," said Silas.

"And so it would. Easier said than done. I'm partly ashamed of talking."

"No, no, you're right, Mrs Winthrop. There is good in the world - more than we can see. I have that feel-

30 ing now."

bring it to my tongue's end, put it into words
folks, people
us that knows, we that know, in standard English

Eppie had been a little girl at school in those years, when Silas and Dolly had sometimes tried to make sense of things. As she grew up, Silas had often talked to her too, about the past. How and why he had lived a lonely man, until she had been sent to him.

He had never tried to hide from her that she was not his own child. She knew all about how her mother had died on the snowy ground, and how she herself had been found on the hearth by father Silas who had thought that her golden curls were his lost guineas.

Eppie had often thought about her mother, who she was, and how she had come to die in the snow. Her knowledge of Mrs Winthrop, who was her nearest friend, next to Silas, made her think that a mother must be a *precious person* to have. She had asked Silas many times to tell her about her mother, what she was like, and how he had found her lying against the furze bush. But she had never thought about the fact that she must have had a father.

The first time that she thought about it at all was when Silas showed her the wedding ring her mother had worn. It had been taken from her mother, kept carefully in a little box, and given to Eppie when she was grown up.

This afternoon, when she came out into the sunshine to look for Silas, the first thing her eyes lit upon was the furze bush. It was still there.

"Father," she said, in a soft and serious tone, "we'll take the furze bush into the garden, won't we? It'll be in the corner. And I'll put *snowdrops* and *crocuses*

precious person, person (she would have) loved
snowdrops, crocuses, garden flowers that bloom in winter (see picture, page 86)

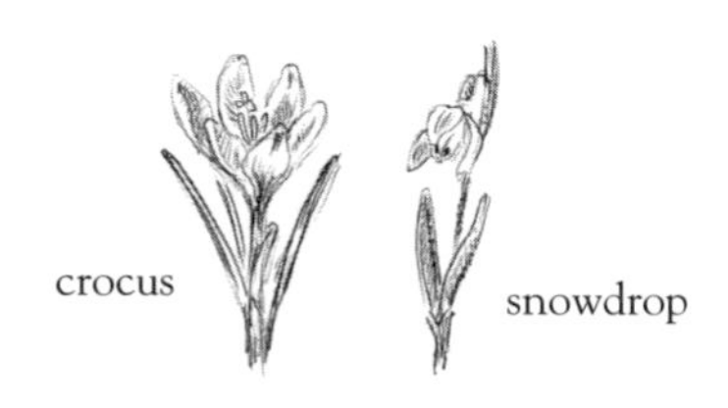

beside it. Aaron says they don't die out - they just get to be more and more."

"It wouldn't do to leave out the furze bush. There's nothing prettier, when it is all covered in yellow flowers. We'll do that, child. Do you know, I was just sitting here thinking about what we were going to do for a fence."

"I'll tell you, Daddy," said Eppie, after a minute's thought, "how about stones? Couldn't we build a wall instead? Aaron could help us carry the big stones."

"A stone wall, eh? I wonder whether we've enough loose stones left around here, after all the building we did."

Eppie went over to the edge of the Stone pit, looking for stones. She wanted to find a fairly large one, so that she could show her father that she was strong enough to help build the wall.

"Just come and look here, Father," she called out in surprise. "Come and see how the water has gone down since yesterday."

"Well, to be sure," said Silas, coming to her side. The water had gone very far down. Mr Cass had bought up the Osgoods' fields, and *draining* had begun after the harvest was finished. "Your pit will be dry as a bone, I

draining, here: to draw water away from land, making it better for farming

shouldn't wonder", the *foreman* had said to him one day. It would certainly make it easier to get hold of more stones.

"How odd it will be, to have the old pit dried up," said Eppie, turning around to pick up a fairly large stone. She was only able to carry it a few steps, however, before she dropped it again.

"See! You are *delicately built*." said Silas, "That's what your godmother says. We'll have to see about the wall. My old arms aren't so strong either."

Eppie took hold of one of his arms and they went over to sit on the bank. "Father," she said, very gently, after they had been sitting in silence for a while, "if I was to be married, ought I to be married with my mother's ring?"

Silas was surprised. Then he realised that, perhaps, he was not so very surprised after all.

"Why, Eppie, have you been thinking about it?" He did not want to say anything that might upset her.

"Only this last week, father. Since Aaron talked to me about it."

"And what did he say?" Silas asked.

"He said that he'd like to be married. He's nearly twenty-four, and he's got a lot of gardening work now. He has two days a week with Mr Cass, one with Mr Osgood. And now they're going to take him on at the Rectory as well."

"And who is it that he wants to marry?" asked Silas, with a little smile.

"Why me, to be sure, Daddy," said Eppie laughing

foreman, person in charge of the work
delicately built, here: with small bones and not very strong

and kissing her father's cheek. "As if he'd want to marry anybody else!"

"And you mean to have him, do you?"

"Yes, some time," said Eppie, "I don't know when. Everybody's married some time, Aaron says. But I told him that wasn't true. Look at Father, I said. He's never been married."

"No, child, your father was a lone man until you were sent to him."

"But you'll never be on your own again, Daddy. That is what Aaron wants. He wants us all to live together, so that you needn't work more than you want to. And he'd be as good as a son to you - that was what he said."

"And would you like that, Eppie?" asked Silas, looking at her.

"I wouldn't mind it, Father," said Eppie, simply. "I don't want you to work too much. If it wasn't for that, I'm happy the way things are. I like Aaron being fond of me and coming to see us so often and being nice to you. He **is** always nice to you, isn't he, Daddy?"

"Yes, child, nobody could behave better. He's his mother's lad."

"But I don't want any change," said Eppie. "I'd like to go on a long time just as we are."

But of course things would change sometime, whether they wanted them to or not. Eppie was young to be thinking of getting married. But Silas would be getting older and more helpless. He would not want to be a burden. He would like to think that Eppie had somebody else besides himself, somebody young and strong, who would take care of her to the end. He tried to explain these thoughts as best as he could.

"Then, would you like me to be married, Father?"

asked Eppie, when he had finished. There was a slight tremble in her voice.

"I'll not be the man to say no, Eppie. Do you know what we'll do? We'll talk to your godmother about it this afternoon. She'll want the best for you, and for Aaron too. If there's a right thing to be done, Mrs Winthrop is the one to work it out."

8

While Silas and Eppie were walking down the lane, keeping an eye out for the arrival of the Winthrops, Nancy Cass was taking a walk in the garden of the Red House. She was chatting to her sister, Priscilla, while they waited for Mr Lammeter to awake from his afternoon sleep.

"I'm so glad that Godfrey is making that exchange of land with the Osgoods'," said Priscilla. "There is nothing like *dairy* farming to take your mind off your other worries. Do you know, you'll never be low when you've got a dairy."

"Well, Prissy, I don't know whether a dairy will ever mean that much to Godfrey! I only feel low, you know, because of the way **he** feels. I'd be happy with the *blessings* we have, if only Godfrey could feel the same way."

This point of view did not seem to please Priscilla at all.

"It drives me mad," said she, "the way men are always wanting something, and then wanting more."

Nancy had not intended that her remarks would lead to an outburst like this. She wanted to explain that it was only natural that Godfrey felt the way he did. He was the best of husbands. Any man would want to have children to work for and to save for.

"Oh Prissy! Godfrey is the best of husbands, It..."

But Priscilla was not in a mood for listening today. "Oh! You're a typical wife, all right," said she. "First you give me every reason to complain about your husband. And then you are ready to turn around and start praising him, as if you were trying to sell him!"

Fortunately, perhaps, at this point they turned the corner of the house. Mr Lammeter was out on the stone steps, chatting to Godfrey, and the *gig* was waiting at the front door.

Godfrey and Nancy promised to visit soon, and

dairy, keeping cows to produce milk, butter and cheese
blessing, something good that is believed to come from God
gig, small cart with two wheels drawn by one horse (see picture, page 91)

stood at the front door waving good-bye.

"I'll just take a walk over to the fields at the Stone pit, and look at the draining," said Godfrey.

"You'll be in again by tea-time, dear?"

"Yes, certainly, I'll be back in an hour." 5

Godfrey usually took a walk or a ride on Sunday afternoons to have a look at one or another part of his lands. Nancy seldom went with him. If Priscilla wasn't there, she usually spent an hour with her Bible, reading quietly, while waiting for afternoon tea. 10

That afternoon, Nancy found it particularly hard to keep her mind on her reading. Things that she wanted Priscilla to understand were running through her head. Godfrey found it hard to accept the fact that they had no children. And it is so much worse for a man to be 15 *disappointed* in that way, Nancy thought. A woman can

disappointed, to have hoped for something one does not get

be satisfied *devoting* herself to her husband. Whereas a man, she felt, seems to want something that will make him look forward more.

Nancy still had a drawer filled with little baby clothes, made by her own hands. She had lost her only baby, soon after its birth, fourteen years earlier. Only one little dress, used as a burial dress for the baby, had been removed. Many years ago now, she had firmly decided not to open that drawer any more.

It was her duty to accept what was given to her in this life. She felt that very strongly. And when she had not been *granted* children, she must accept the situation as it was.

She had tried many times to explain her feelings about this to Godfrey. But, as always, when she thought about it, she arrived at the same question. Had she done everything in her power to make things easier for Godfrey? Had she been right six years ago to go against his wish to *adopt* a child? And again four years ago, when she had argued long against this idea of his.

Nancy hated to go against her husband's wishes. But to adopt a child because you had no children of your own was wrong. She was deeply *convinced* of this. If you had not been granted what you hoped for in this life, it was your duty to accept that. You should not try to choose your own *lot in life*. There must be some higher reason, she felt, why they were better without a child.

devoting, giving all of one's time and interest to something or to somebody
granted, here: given by God
to adopt, to make a member of your family
convinced, certain that something is right
lot in life, what you are given in life

If they adopted one, it would never turn out well.

"But why should you think that the child would not turn out well?" Godfrey had wanted to know. "Eppie has turned out as well as any child can do, with the weaver. And he adopted her." 5

"Yes, my dear Godfrey," she had replied, on the verge of tears, "but the weaver did not go to seek her out, as we would be doing. Please don't ask me to do what I know is wrong."

Nancy had reminded her husband that the only other adoption they had ever heard of had turned out very badly. A woman they had met at Royston Baths, several years ago, had told them about her sister's child. This sister had adopted a boy who had been *transported* when he was twenty-three years old. 15

But Godfrey had made it clear from the start that the child he thought suitable for them to adopt was Eppie, then about twelve years old. He had pointed out that she was the prettiest girl in the parish. That no child could be better fitted for adoption into the Cass family. 20 But he had never brought himself to tell Nancy the full truth of the matter. She might never recover from the shock, he feared, if she were to hear the story of his earlier marriage.

During all the discussions that had taken place 25 between them, not much mention had ever been made of Silas Marner. Neither Godfrey nor Nancy had given much thought to the question of what feelings he might have about the idea.

Godfrey was inclined to think that the weaver 30

transported, here: forced to leave the country as a punishment for breaking the law

would, of course, want the best for the child. And according to his own way of thinking, there could not be a better fortune for any child, than that of belonging to the best family in Raveloe. He was not an unkind person at heart. But he would have been very surprised indeed to learn that people who lived in a poor stone cottage had any deep feelings.

Nancy had little reason to consider the weaver's feelings at all. She was against the whole idea of the adoption. If God had wanted her to become a mother, as she saw it, her baby would not have died or she would have had another baby. Not that her understanding of the will of God came from any deep reading on the matter; it lay deeply in her way of thinking, even about the most ordinary matters. She would give up her plan to shop at a particular place, if it rained three times in a row on the days when she had planned to go there. The rain, she would say, was probably a sign that she should not go to that place. And to Nancy, her childlessness was a sign of where her difficult duty lay.

"I wonder if Godfrey will mind it more as he gets older?" she asked herself, that afternoon. "I'm afraid, more..." she was thinking, when the servant, Jane, suddenly appeared with the tea things.

"Has your master come into the yard, Jane?" asked Nancy, in some surprise that it could be so late.

"No, ma'am, he hasn't."

Jane set the table for tea, making more noise about it than usual. She seemed to have something on her mind.

"I don't know whether you've seen them, ma'am. Everyone has been rushing down the street for the last ten minutes. There isn't a man in the yard. I hope

nobody is hurt, that's all. But something has happened."

"No, I haven't. Probably nothing much is the matter."

When Jane had gone, however, Nancy went to the front window and looked as far as she could see. There was no sign of anybody at all now. That was strange. And certainly it was later than she had thought. She was afraid that something might, after all, have happened.

The door opened behind her. Nancy turned around in relief.

"Dear, I'm so thankful you've come. I began to get..."

She stopped suddenly. For it was immediately clear that Godfrey had had the most dreadful shock. His face was very pale and he was looking at her with a strange glance. She laid a hand on his arm, not daring to speak.

"Sit down, Nancy - there," he said, after a few

moments, pointing to a chair opposite his own. He sat down himself.

"I came back as soon as I could. I didn't want anybody else to tell you. I've had a great shock. But I care most about the shock it will be to you."

"It isn't father and Priscilla...?"

"No, no, it's nobody living."

Godfrey took a deep breath before he could go on.

"It's Dunstan - my brother Dunstan, who disappeared sixteen years ago. We've found him. Found his body - his *skeleton*."

Nancy did not know what she had feared, when she had seen the look on Godfrey's face. But something worse than this. She waited more calmly to hear the rest.

"The Stone-pit has gone dry suddenly - from the draining, I suppose. And there he lies - has lain for sixteen years, *wedged* between some rocks. There is his watch and my hunting whip, with my name on it. He took it with him the day he went hunting on Wildfire, the last time he was seen."

Godfrey paused. It was not easy to tell the next part.

"Do you think he drowned himself, Godfrey?" Nancy had heard several strange ideas in the past about what this unloved brother might have done.

"No, he fell in," said Godfrey in a low voice. Then he added: "Dunstan was the man that robbed Silas Marner."

The blood rushed to Nancy's face, in surprise and shame.

skeleton, the bones of a body
wedged, stuck

"Godfrey!" she said, feeling sorry for him at once. The shame, of course, was worse for him. Dunstan was his brother.

"The money was in the pit," he went on, "all the weaver's money. Everything has been taken up. They are bringing the skeleton to the Rainbow. I had to come back to tell you. It never once crossed my mind... that he could do such a thing! I should have thought..."

Godfrey said no more, staring at the floor. Nancy was silent, feeling that he had something more to tell her.

"Everything comes to light, Nancy, sooner or later. When God Almighty wills it, our secrets are found out." He lifted his eyes to her face. "I've lived with a secret that I'll keep from you no longer," he went on, "I wouldn't want you to find out after I'm dead."

Nancy's feeling of dread had come back. There was something more terrible to come.

"Nancy," he said, slowly, "when I married you, I hid something from you that I ought to have told you. That woman Marner found dead in the snow - Eppie's mother - was my wife. Eppie is my child."

Nancy sat quite still. Her eyes dropped and no longer met his. She sat clasping her hands on her lap.

"You'll never think the same of me again."

Still, Nancy said nothing.

"I ought to have acknowledged the child. She should have been one of us. I ought not to have kept it from you. I just couldn't bear to give you up, Nancy. I was led into marrying her - I suffered for it."

Nancy was still silent. He sat waiting for her to say something. Perhaps she would leave and go to her father's house. His faults must seem so black to her.

Dear Nancy, was such a good person. But when she spoke, it was quietly and with *regret*.

"Godfrey, if you had told me this six years ago, we could have done some of our *duty* by that child. Do you think I'd have refused to take her in, if I'd known that she was yours?"

At that moment, Godfrey realised that his secret, kept for so long, was without any point at all. His wife was indeed a kind and good person - more so than he had ever known.

"And do you know," Nancy went on, "if we'd had her from the start, she'd have loved me as her mother. You'd have been happier with me. Our life might be more like what we used to think it would be." Nancy's voice shook a little on her last words, and her tears began to fall.

"But you wouldn't have married me then, Nancy, if I'd told you," said Godfrey, gently.

"I don't know, Godfrey. I just don't know. I would certainly never have married anyone else. But I wasn't worth doing wrong for anyway - nothing is in this world."

They sat in silence for a while, their tea left untouched.

"Maybe nothing is as good as it seems before it happens," said Nancy, with a sad smile, "not even our getting married, you see."

"Can you forgive me, ever?"

"You've made up for it to **me**, Godfrey. You've been good to me for fifteen years. It's the child I'm thinking

regret, sorrow about the past
duty, to do something that you owe to somebody else because they have a right to it

of. Can it ever be made up to her?"

"But we can take Eppie now," said Godfrey. "I won't mind the world knowing at last. I'm going to be an open person for the rest of my life. No more secrets! From now on, Eppie shall have what is her right." 5

"It'll be different, of course, now that she is grown up." Nancy shook her head sadly. "But it's your duty to provide for her. And I'll pray to God Almighty to make her love me."

"We'll go together to Silas Marner's this very night, 10 as soon as everything is quiet at the Stone-pit."

9

By eight o'clock that evening, Eppie and Silas were once more on their own in the cottage. Mrs Winthrop and Aaron, who had stayed on longer than all the other visitors that afternoon, had also left for home. All 15 the excitement of that day had now given way to a strange look of wonder on Silas's face.

He sat looking at Eppie, who had drawn her own chair towards him and was leaning forward to hold both his hands. The gold lay on the table beside them, lit by a candle. It was ordered in a square, just like the time when Silas had counted it every night, before Eppie was sent to him.

"At first, you know," Silas was saying, "I had a feeling now and then that you might be changed into the gold again. I would see gold, you see, no matter which way I turned my head. I thought I might be glad to feel the coins again. But that didn't last long."

"Did you not want to see them back again?"

"Well, I would have thought it was a *curse* come again, if it had driven you away from me," said Silas. "I'd got to feel the need of your smile, your little voice and the touch of your little fingers, you see. You were such a little one then, Eppie. You didn't know what your old father Silas felt for you."

"But I know now," said Eppie, giving his hands a squeeze, "if there'd been nobody to love me then, they'd have taken me to the workhouse."

"Eh, the blessing was all mine. I'd have gone to the grave in my *misery*, if you hadn't been sent to me. But isn't it wonderful - how the money was taken away from me in time, and then kept until it was needed for you! Isn't our life a wonder?"

Silas sat for some minutes, looking over at the money.

curse, a cause of evil
misery, great suffering and unhappiness

"It takes no hold of me at all now," he said. "I don't suppose it ever will. Unless I lost you Eppie. Then I might lose the feeling that God was good to me."

Snap began growling in his corner. There was a knock at the door. Eppie got up to answer it. Silas could see that she was opening the door wide and making a shy little *curtsy*. It was Mr and Mrs Cass.

"We're calling very late, my dear," said Mrs Cass, looking rather pale, taking Eppie's hand, and gazing at her face with interest.

Eppie placed chairs for Mr and Mrs Cass, opposite Silas, and went over to stand beside his chair.

"Well, Marner," Godfrey began, "I'm very pleased indeed to see that you have your money again. It was one of my family that did you wrong. I feel I have to make up to you for it in every way. I will only be paying my debts."

He and Nancy had agreed not to tell them that he himself was Eppie's father. If at all possible, this should be made known, gradually, in the future. Nancy had wanted it this way, feeling that the relationship between her mother and father would be a subject that was painful to Eppie.

"Sir, I have plenty to thank you for already," said Silas. "The robbery was no loss to me. And even if it was, that was no fault of yours." He felt very uncomfortable speaking to a man like Mr Cass in his own cottage. That sort of person was normally seen at a distance - and on horseback.

curtsy, a movement of the body made by women as a sign of respect to somebody of importance

"You may look at it that way, Marner. But I have my own ideas about what is just. You've worked hard all your life. But you are getting rather past that kind of work, perhaps? Though you're not an old man, **are** you?" 5

"Fifty-five, as near as I can say, sir," said Silas.

"Why, you may live another thirty years or more - look at old Macey! That money on the table won't go far, even if you only had yourself to keep. But you've had two to keep for a good many years now." 10

This line of thought was not making much of an impression on Silas.

"Eh, sir, we do very well, Eppie and me. I don't know what it would be to *gentlefolks*. But there's few working folks that have that much money saved up. It's almost 15 too much for us. There's little we want."

"Only the garden, father," said Eppie. And then she blushed up to her ears a moment later, realising that this was quite the wrong thing to say and do.

"You love a garden, do you, my dear?" said Nancy, 20 brightly, thinking that this subject might help things along. "We would certainly agree on that. I give a great deal of time to the garden."

"Ah, yes, there's plenty of gardening at the Red House," said Godfrey, wondering how he was going to 25 get back to his subject again. He had thought that this situation would be easier to handle. He cleared his throat.

"Well, Marner, you've looked after Eppie for sixteen years. It would be a great comfort to you to see her well 30

gentlefolks, people from good families, usually well off and brought up with fine manners

provided for, wouldn't it? She doesn't look like a girl that has come from working parents. You'd like to see her taken care of by those who could make a lady of her, wouldn't you? She's more fit for that, than for the rough life she might come to have in a few years' time, eh? "

"I don't know exactly what you mean, sir," said Silas, feeling hurt and uneasy, and not knowing what to say.

"My meaning is this, Marner. Mrs Cass and I, as you know, have no children - nobody to share our good home and everything else we have. We would like to have somebody in the place of a daughter to us. We would like to have Eppie, and treat her as our own child."

Silas sat in *stunned* silence. Eppie, who had put a hand on his shoulder, could feel that he was trembling.

"I'm sure it would comfort you in your old age to see her fortune made in that way," Godfrey continued. "And Eppie, I'm sure, will always love you and be grateful to you. She'll come to see you very often."

The silence continued once more. Eppie was just going to lean down and whisper to him, when Silas spoke in a faint voice.

"Eppie, my child, speak. I won't stand in your way. Thank Mr and Mrs Cass."

Eppie took a step forward and curtsied first to Mrs Cass and then to Mr Cass. She had lost the shyness she had felt when they had first arrived, being more taken up with her father's feelings than those of the visitors.

"Thank you, ma'am, thank you, sir," she said. "But I can't leave my father, nor be closer to anyone than

stunned, deeply shocked and unable to speak

him. And I don't want to be a lady. Thank you all the same."

Eppie curtsied once more to the visitors. "I couldn't give up the folks I've been used to," she added, as she came back once more to her father's chair and put her hand on his shoulder again. Silas put up his hand to grasp hers.

Nancy dared not say a word. She could understand Eppie's feelings. She felt less sure of how poor Godfrey might be feeling. He had been so taken up with the idea of *mending* his ways and doing the right thing at last.

to mend, to put into good condition again

If Godfrey was feeling anything other than surprise, it was anger.

"But I've a claim on you Eppie - the strongest of all claims. It's my duty, Marner, to acknowledge Eppie as 5 my child and to provide for her. She's my child. Her mother was my wife. My claim must stand before every other."

"Then, sir, why didn't you say so sixteen years ago?" asked Silas. Suddenly, he seemed to have lost all doubt 10 and uncertainty. Eppie, standing behind his shoulder, had turned quite pale.

"Why didn't you claim her before I had come to love her?" Silas went on. "Instead of coming to claim her now - you might as well take the heart out of my body. 15 When a man turns a blessing from his door, it falls to them who take it in."

"I know that, Marner. I was wrong. I've repented my action in that matter." Godfrey couldn't help admitting to himself that Marner had put his finger on a sore spot.

20 "I'm glad to hear it, sir. But your coming here now and saying 'I'm her father' doesn't change what's been going on inside us for sixteen years. I'm the one that she's called her father ever since she could say the word."

25 "I do think you might look at the thing more reasonably, Marner," said Godfrey, who certainly had not expected to hear this kind of home truth from the weaver. "It isn't as though you'll never see her again. She'll come and see you very often. She'll feel just the 30 same towards you."

This, as Silas saw it, was nothing but the greatest nonsense. "Just the same?" said he, in a bitter tone that Eppie had never heard from him before. "How'll she feel the same for me as she does now, when we eat from the same dish, drink from the same cup, and think the same things from one day's end to the other? That's *idle talk*. You'd cut us in two."

"I would have thought, Marner, that you would be happy, since it is for her own good," said Godfrey, very stiffly. "Even," he added, "if it calls upon you to give up something."

It seemed to Godfred that the weaver was being quite selfish. Perhaps his point should be made more clearly.

"You are putting yourself in the way of her *welfare*. You ought to remember, Marner, that you are at an age when your own life is uncertain. She is at an age where her lot may soon be fixed - why, she may even marry some low working man! And then it would be very difficult for me to provide for her. It is my duty to insist on taking care of my own daughter."

Eppie was listening carefully to this strange *contest* between her old long-loved father and this new father who had suddenly appeared. While her eyes looked from one to the other, her mind darted backwards and forwards. What was it that was being offered to her instead of the life she knew? Her mind was quite made up. But these last words of her new father had helped to make clearer the life he had in mind for her. They had also made clear to her that he was not the kind of person she would want to care for.

The same words had shocked Silas. Could it be true, that he was a selfish person standing in the way of

idle talk, nonsense
welfare, comfort and well-being
contest, competition

Eppie's good? It was difficult for him to put his thoughts into words. At last he felt able to try.

"I'll say no more. Let it be as you will. Speak to the child. I'll not come between you."

Nancy and Godfrey Cass heard these words with a great sense of relief. Nancy could quite understand that it had been hard on the poor weaver. But they had got their wish. From now on Eppie would be provided for in the manner to which she had a perfect right. Nancy was as fully convinced of the justice of this as her husband was.

"Eppie, my dear," Godfrey began. He felt uneasy at the idea that his daughter was quite old enough to judge him. "Eppie, my dear, it will always be our wish that you should show your love and gratitude to the one who has been a father to you for so many years. We hope that you will come to love us as well. I'll do everything in my power to provide for you as my only child. And you'll have the best of mothers in my wife."

"My dear, you will be a treasure to me," said Nancy, in her gentle way. "We'll want for nothing when we have our daughter."

Eppie did not step forward and curtsy this time. She spoke in a colder tone than before, still holding Silas's hand. It was a weaver's hand, with fingers that were sensitive to the touch.

"Thank you, ma'am - thank you, sir - for your offers. They are very great. Far more than I want. But I'd have no pleasure in life any more if I was forced to go away from my father, when I knew that he was sitting at home thinking of me. We're used to being happy together every day. He took care of me from the first, and I want to stay with him as long as he lives."

"But you have to be sure, Eppie," said Silas in a low voice. "You must be sure that you won't ever be sorry to have stayed among poor folks. You could have everything of the best, you know."

"How could I be sorry, Father?" All this argument was beginning to make her *impatient.*

"I wouldn't know what to think of or wish for, with fine things all around me that I'm not used to. Can you see me putting on those things and riding in a gig? I'd have to sit in a different place in the church. The people I'm fond of would think that they couldn't even speak to me! How do you think I'd feel then?"

Nancy looked over at Godfrey with a pained look in her questioning eyes. But he was staring at the end of his walking stick. "What you say is natural, my dear child," she said. "But there is a duty you owe to your lawful father," she went on. "When he opens his home to you, it is right that you don't turn your back on it."

"But I can't feel that I've got more than one father," said Eppie, almost in tears. "I've always thought of a little home where he'd sit in the corner and I'd do everything for him. I can't think of any other home. I wasn't brought up to be a lady, and I can't turn my mind to it. I like the working folks and their food and their ways."

Eppie's tears had started to roll down her face. But she still had not said everything that she wanted to make these people understand. "And I'm promised to marry a working man, who'll live with us and help me to take care of Father," she finished.

Godfrey finally looked up. "Let us go," he said in a hissing whisper to Nancy. He walked to the door.

impatient, unable to wait for something to end or to happen

"We won't talk of this any longer just now," said Nancy getting up to go. "We wish you well, my dear, and you tòo, Marner. We'll come and see you again. It's getting late now." Nancy hoped that these words would help to cover up the way her husband was suddenly leaving the cottage. For Godfrey had gone straight to the door, unable to say any more.

* * *

Not a word was said between Nancy and Godfrey as they made their way back down the lane to the village. Godfrey did not break the silence until he was back in the parlour of the Red House, sitting in his armchair.

"So, that's ended."

"Yes," said Nancy, taking his hand, "I'm afraid that we must give up the hope of having her for our daughter. We can't change the way she's been brought up and what has come of it. It wouldn't be right to force her."

"No, it's too late now. Marner was right when he said that a blessing falls to somebody else, when you turn it away from your own door."

For some moments, Nancy had no reply to this.

"You're not going to make it known then," she asked at last, "about Eppie being your daughter?" This was the question she had been trying not to think about, as they walked back from the Stone-pit to the Red House.

"No, there wouldn't be any point," said Godfrey. "I'll just have to do the best I can for her. I think I should put it in my *will* though. I don't like the idea of things being found out afterwards - like this about Dunstan."

will, a paper in which is written down what is to be done with the things of value that one owns after one has died

"No, everyone will hear about that. But I'd be pleased, of course, if father and Priscilla didn't have the trouble of knowing the rest, about what happened in the past."

"Of course not. We'll just have to do our best, in a quiet way, to make her happy in her own way. Do you know, I think it's the young gardener, Aaron Winthrop, that she's engaged to. I saw them walking away from the church together."

"Well, he's a very nice young man, and very hard-working," said Nancy, cheering up a bit as she thought about this.

"And she is a very pretty, nice girl, isn't she, Nancy?"

"Yes, dear. And she has just the same hair and eyes as you. I hadn't thought about that before this evening."

"She did not like the idea that I was her father, though. She took a dislike to me when I told them."

Nancy had thought the same, but did not like to say so.

"She didn't like to think of her father being anyone else but Marner," she said, gently.

5 "It's part of my punishment, I think, that my daughter dislikes me. There was a time when I wanted people to think I had no children. And now when..."

Godfrey didn't seem able to say any more, just then. Nancy gave his hand a little squeeze. "I'd be so happy, 10 Godfrey," she said, "if you could accept our lives the way they are."

"I've got you, Nancy," said Godfrey, smiling at last. "And I've been *grumbling*... Well, maybe it isn't too late to mend some things. It is too late to mend some other 15 things. That's certain."

10

There was one time of the year that people in Raveloe thought was the most suitable time for a wedding. That was when the *lilacs* and the *laburnums* were in bloom, and purple and gold flowers hung over the garden walls. 20 The young calves needed all the milk they could get at that time of year. The cheese-making could not start yet, and people were not so busy.

The sun shone more warmly than usual on the morning that Eppie was married. This was fortunate, 25 since her dress was a very light one. Seen from a distance, as she came out of the church on Aaron's arm, the dress looked pure white. In fact there were tiny lit-

grumbling, talking about things that annoy one or do not make one glad
lilac, *laburnum*, small trees with flowers that bloom in late spring or early summer (see picture, page 113)

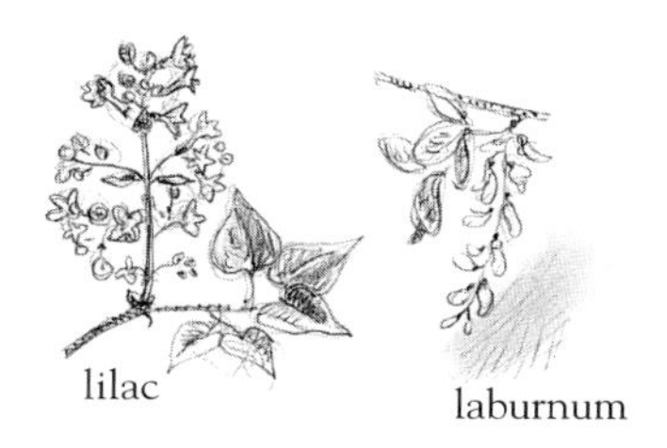

tle pink buds sewn on it, here and there. You could only see them if you looked closely.

This was exactly the dress that Eppie had seen in her mind's eye. But she never thought she would have one like it. So when Mrs Cass begged to be allowed to provide the wedding dress, Eppie had known exactly what she wanted. 5

Now, as she crossed the churchyard, she had one hand on the arm of her husband and she held Silas's hand with the other. The dress seemed to be of the purest white, and her hair looked like the dash of gold on a *lily*. Dolly Winthrop walked behind them with her husband. 10

"Now, you won't be giving me away, Father," Eppie had said before they went to the church. "You'll only be taking Aaron to be a son to you." 15

They were going to walk through the village now, and then have a quiet pause at the stone cottage. The wedding feast would be in an hour's time at the Rainbow. 20

There were many eyes to see them. Priscilla Lammeter was glad that she and her father happened to arrive in their gig at the Red House, just in time to see the

lily, white garden flower with a golden yellow centre

pretty sight. They were calling in to see Nancy, because she would be on her own today.

It was a pity, thought Priscilla, that Godfrey had to go to Lytherly for some special reason just today. Otherwise he might have liked to join Mr Crackenthorp and Mr Osgood for a drink later on. They would almost certainly be going to the Rainbow to see how the wedding feast was getting along. After all, Godfrey Cass had ordered the feast. It was natural that he should feel an interest in the weaver, who had been robbed by one of the Cass family.

"I wish Nancy had had the luck to find a child like that and bring her up," said Priscilla to her father, as they sat in the gig watching the bridal group coming down the path of the church.

"Yes, my dear, yes," said Mr Lammeter, "one feels that as one gets older. It's nice to have young people about you to let you know that the world is the same as it used to be."

Nancy came out now to welcome her father and sister. The wedding group had passed on beyond the Red House to the part of the village where the cottages got smaller and smaller.

Old Mr Macey was sitting in his arm-chair, outside his own door, in the sun. He was too old now to be able to come to the wedding feast.

"Mr Macey will expect a word as we pass," whispered Dolly to the three in front.

They all went over to shake hands with the old man. Dolly was quite right, of course. Mr Macey had been looking forward to the day and had his speech ready.

"Well, Master Marner," he said, "I've lived to see my words come true. I was the first to say that there was no harm in you, even though your looks are against you. And I was the first to say that you'd get your money back. And it's nothing but right that you should. I wish all of you all the good luck in the world."

While they all shook hands with Mr Macey, the party of guests turned in to the open yard in front of the Rainbow. There would be plenty of time to enjoy a drink, a joke and a chat while they waited for the feast to start. Many of them were telling each other once more the strange story of Silas Marner - how a man brought a blessing on himself when he acted like a father to a lone motherless child.

"When a man deserves his good luck," said Mr Snell, "then it is up to his neighbours to wish him joy."

A loud cheer was heard in the yard, as the wedding group neared the Rainbow. "Go on in. It's all right," said Dolly to her husband. Ben Winthrop, who enjoyed a good joke more than a quiet pause, turned in to join the party at the Rainbow.

Eppie and Aaron, followed by Dolly and Silas, walked up the narrow lane that led to the cottage at the Stone-pit. Eppie was pointing out the flowers she liked best and telling Aaron, once again, how much nicer it was in this part of the world than in the awful town her father came from.

Last year, when his guineas had been found, Silas had decided to make the long journey back to the town from which he came. He had taken Eppie with him, hoping to find Lantern Yard and the minister, Mr Paston. Something might have happened to let them all know that he was innocent of the robbery that had happened that time, long ago.

"You'd be easier in your mind for the rest of your life,

Master Marner," Dolly had said on the day they started their journey. "If there is any light to be got, we've need of it in this world. I'd be glad of it myself, if you could bring it back." But Silas and Eppie had not succeeded in what they hoped to do.

They had walked through the streets of the huge dirty town, finding their way with difficulty. Most of the shops had changed and there were a great many new buildings. The town seemed bigger than Silas remembered it.

Eppie thought it the most dark and ugly place she

had ever seen. The buildings seemed to hide the sky. She found it hard to believe that people lived like this, so close together. But it was the bad smell that surprised Silas. He wondered whether it had been like this when he was a young man, or whether it had got worse. He began walking faster looking for signs that he remembered. 5

At last they reached the right lane. The *nick* in the street where the water ran was still there. And the little shop with the strange window that hung out over the street was there too. But then Silas had stood *stock still.* They were standing in front of a factory building. "Dear heart!" said Silas, staring at the building. 10

He had to explain to Eppie, and later to Dolly, that this was the place where Lantern Yard had been. He had found it hard to believe at first. But there could be no doubt. The chapel and the other buildings were all gone. 15

Nobody they asked had been able to tell them whether the chapel had been closed down or moved to a different place. And nobody seemed to know a minister by the name of Paston. In the end, they returned to Raveloe, no wiser than when they set out on their journey. 20

"*It's all dark to me* still, Mrs Winthrop," Silas said sadly when he had come back to Raveloe and told their story. "I'll never know whether they ever found out the truth about the robbery." 25

"Well, yes, Master Marner, it looks like you'll never

nick, cut
stock still, unable to move
it's dark to you, you do not or cannot understand it

know the rights of it," Dolly said. "But that doesn't mean that there **are** no rights, Master Marner, even though it's dark to you and me."

"No, that doesn't mean that there are no rights. Since the child was sent to me, I've had light enough to trust by," Silas had replied.

That had been in the autumn. Today, there was plenty of time to enjoy the sights and sounds and smells of early summer, as the wedding party made their way up the lane to the Stone-pit. Eppie always enjoyed telling Aaron about the horrors of the big town. He was wiser than she was about many things. But he had never been that far away from Raveloe. Suddenly she stopped. They had turned the corner of the lane and come within sight of her garden.

Eppie had got a much larger garden than she expected. A stone wall ran down from the cottage on both sides. An open fence ran along the front, with a little gate set into it. The flowers could be seen through the fence. They seemed to shine with an answering gladness as the four people came within sight of them.

"Father," said Eppie, "what a pretty home ours is! I think nobody could be happier than we are."

Questions (1)

1. What happened to Silas when he was a young man? How do you think this changed him?

2. Have you ever been accused of doing something you did not do? How did you feel? How do you think Silas felt?

3. What do you think your life would be like if you lived in Raveloe at that time? What was Silas's life like?

4. Why were the local children afraid of Silas? Can you explain why the grown-ups were also afraid of him?

5. Why did Silas begin to save all his money and spend so little?

Questions (2)

1. Why did Godfrey Cass lend the rent money to Dunstan?

2. Why was Godfrey afraid to tell his father about his problems? Why did Dunstan not tell?

3. What was Dunstan's first plan to raise the money? What went wrong with this plan?

4. How did Dunstan make his way back from Batherly to Raveloe? What made his journey so difficult?

5. Why did Dunstan go to Silas Marner's cottage? What did he do there?

Questions (3)

1. Why did Silas leave his house that night? And why did he not lock his door?

2. Did anything ever happen to you that was so awful that, at first, you could not believe it?

3. What made Silas think that Jem Rodney had stolen his money? Why did he change his mind? What made the people at the Rainbow sure that Jem Rodney was not the thief?

4. What did the people of Raveloe do about finding the thief? Were they more fair in their way of going about this than the members of the chapel had been?

5. How did Silas feel during the days after the robbery? Were the people in the village still afraid of him?

Questions (4)

1. What made Godfrey decide at last to tell his father all about his problems?

2. What did he in fact tell his father? Why do you think he did not tell the whole story?

3. What did his father think Godfrey should do? Why was Godfrey still worried after he had talked to him?

4. Why do you think Dolly went to visit Silas? Do you think her visit helped Silas in any way? Why do you think the author wants us to understand this visit in such detail?

5. What do you think of the way that Silas spent his Christmas Day?

Questions (5)

1. What made Nancy think she would never get married?

2. Why did Molly look forward to the idea of walking in to Squire's party at New Year with her child?

3. What made her take her last phial of opium during her journey? How did this affect her? This is the second journey from Batherly to Raveloe described by the author. What is the reason, do you think, for building up the story in this way?

4. What did Silas think when he found the little child on the floor in front of his fire? What did he do? And how did he feel as the evening wore on?

5. What did Godfrey think and do that evening from the moment when he saw his child at the New Year's Party?

Questions (6)

1. Why did Dolly think Silas should keep the child that came to his cottage on New Year's Eve? What did the other people in the village think?

2. How was Dolly able to help Silas?

3. Why was it difficult for Dolly and Silas to understand what the other meant. Can you find examples of this?

4. What did Silas do to make it easier to look after Eppie while he was working? Did he punish her for being naughty when she was a little girl? What did he do and what did he not want to do?

5. How did people's feelings towards Silas change after he became a father to Eppie? How did Silas himself change?

Questions (7)

1. What did Godfrey Cass do for Silas Marner during the years when Eppie was growing up? Why? And what did people in the village think of it?

2. Why do you think Silas began to do all the things that the people in Raveloe thought he should do?

3. What did Dolly and Silas think about what had happened to him as a young man, when they began talking about it?

4. What thoughts did Eppie have about her mother and her father?

5. How did Silas feel about Eppie's plans for marriage?

Questions (8)

1. How did Nancy feel about the fact that she and Godfrey did not have any children?

2. How did Godfrey feel? And what solution to the problem could he see? Why was he so taken up with this idea? And why, do you think, did he give such little thought to what Silas Marner's reaction would be?

3. How were the people of Raveloe able to find out whose body it was in the Stone-pit, when the water went down? How did the author plan the story in such a way that this would be possible?

4. What made Godfrey tell Nancy the full truth at last? How did she react? What did they decide to do?

5. How did Nancy feel about the idea of adoption? Why do you think she felt this way? Do you think she was right to feel the way she did?

Questions (9)

1. How did Silas react when his money was found?

2. How did Silas react at first to Godfrey Cass's suggestion? How did Eppie react?

3. Why do you think Godfrey decided to say that he was Eppie's father? How did Silas and Eppie react to this news?

4. What arguments did Godfrey use to persuade Silas and Eppie to accept his plan? What do you think of his arguments? What did Silas think of them?

5. What feelings did Eppie have? If you were in Eppie's position, do you think you would have had the same feelings or would you have felt differently?

Questions (10)

1. Why do you think Godfrey went away on the day Eppie got married? Was Priscilla right in thinking that he would have liked to have gone to the Rainbow that day?

2. Mr Lammeter thought that young people remind old people that the world is the same as it used to be. Do you think young people still do this?

3. How did the people of Raveloe feel towards Silas Marner on Eppie's wedding day?

4. Why do you think Silas decided to visit the town he came from? How did Eppie feel about the differences between life in the town and life in the countryside?

5. What do you imagine Eppie's life will be like in the future?